Peter Kapitsa
on
Life and Science

Peter Kapitsa
on
Life and Science

Addresses and Essays Collected, Translated,
and Annotated with an Introduction

BY

ALBERT PARRY

The Macmillan Company, New York
Collier-Macmillan Ltd., London

Library of Congress Catalog Card Number: 68-23640

FIRST PRINTING

The Macmillan Company, New York

Collier-Macmillan Canada Ltd., Toronto, Ontario

Printed in the United States of America

Contents

III
TWO INTERVIEWS

Peter Kapitsa
on
Life and Science

Introduction

Peter Kapitsa:
The Man and His Work

I

If you ask any scientist anywhere, East or West, for the name of the Soviet scientist best known to him, chances are overwhelmingly for the answer: "Peter Kapitsa, of course." The name is indeed well known the world over, but not the man himself. Despite all the many years of his appearance in the world's headlines, Academician Pyotr Leonidovich Kapitsa is something of a mystery, and not only to other nations but to his fellow Russians as well.

One of the earliest Russians to come back to the Soviet Union from a prolonged experience abroad, and surely one of the most important among such repatriates, Kapitsa has never publicly explained certain intriguing details of his return in 1934. And because such details are still not quite clear, they have to be reported in this work by hearsay and almost on speculation.

The extent of Kapitsa's reconciliation with the Communist regime which practically kidnaped him is an enigma. To some observers, equally debatable is the degree to which he may be viewed as a center or a symbol of present-day active opposition of one group within the New Class against another, of scientists against political bosses.

Some say that the great Russian physicist is a loyal Soviet patriot, even if not a member of the Communist Party. At least one of the Russian defectors with whom I have talked expressed his doubt that Peter Kapitsa can be properly regarded as a source of opposition to the Party. This man, a former industrial manager from Leningrad, remarked to me that Dr. Kapitsa "has been vastly overrated as harboring any true sense" of any such opposition; "there is no real independence in him."

But I have found this a minority opinion. Others, in speaking about Kapitsa, recall the strange story of his kidnaping by Joseph Stalin, cite instances of his defiance of Stalin and his later differences with Nikita Khrushchev, and insist that he is still a rebel—a kind of "Peck's Bad Boy" of the Soviets.

In the last few years Kapitsa has publicly denounced Communist dogmatists for their Stalin-begotten hostility to Einstein's theory of relativity, to electronic computers, to cybernetics as a whole. He has criticized Khrushchevian and post-Khrushchevian interference by Communist politicians in the daily affairs and long-range plans of Soviet science. He has made no secret of liking the officially tabooed work of Soviet abstractionist artists and sculptors. In sum, the available evidence points to the fact that in his long but not too voluntary Soviet period Peter Kapitsa has at times gone against the power that has tried to order him around. If not always in opposition, and certainly not the chief leader of any hidden or open "scientists' movement" against the Kremlin, Peter Kapitsa by his life and work does prove that the New Class is divided.[1]

II

There are plenty of reasons why both Communists and non-Communists should admire Professor Kapitsa. Director of the

Peter Kapitsa: The Man and His Work

Academy's far-famed Institute of Problems of Physics, he is one of Russia's foremost physicists, author of the hydrodynamic theory of bearing lubrication, originator of the hypothesis of spherical lightning, researcher and designer of equipment in heat transfer and superfluidity of helium, and leading experimenter in atomic physics. His scholarly publications are numerous and important, and his work has earned for him a great number of Soviet and international honors and prizes.

Pyotr Leonidovich Kapitsa, born in July 8, 1894, comes of West Russian blood—from Belorussia, or White Russia. Peter's father, Leonid, was a lieutenant general in the Tsar's Corps of Engineers; he helped to modernize the old naval base and fortress of Kronstadt, near St. Petersburg (now Leningrad). His mother Olga was a well-known teacher and collector of Russian folklore. Peter was born at Kronstadt. Some of the best schools of tsarist Russia gave him his early education.

The revolution of 1917 found Peter an honor student in the capital's Polytechnic Institute. His first scientific paper was published in the journal of the Russian Society of Physics and Chemistry the very month the Bolsheviks overthrew the liberal Provisional Government and proclaimed their Soviet republic. Kapitsa's official Communist biographer was, in time, to comment: "Life presents most incredible coincidences. Along with the new state a new scientist was born." [2]

Graduating in 1918, the young man worked with Professor Abram F. Ioffe [3] in the Physics-Technical Institute. Ioffe was Russia's earliest atomic physicist. By his side Kapitsa learned as much about the elusive atom as was known at the time. He also worked with Professor Nikolai Semyonov,[4] who many years later (in 1956) won a Nobel Prize. In 1918-20 Semyonov and Kapitsa collaborated in the development of an original method of ascertaining magnetic properties of the atom.

But Russia's civil war and its aftermath were not exactly conducive to the scientists' well-being and peace of mind. Amid the bloodshed and chaos of 1918-21 the Kremlin had little thought for Russian savants. Grandiose plans of government-

3

sponsored research remained on paper. For many scholars and their families there was neither food nor fuel. Some died amid privations. Several reports insist that among such victims were Kapitsa's wife and two babies, and that Peter himself survived almost in spite of his will. Crushed, brooding, he decided to leave his homeland.

Soviet officials at first wouldn't hear of a foreign journey for Kapitsa. Now that the civil war was over, the Soviet republic needed scientists for its reconstruction, they said. But Maxim Gorky, Russia's most influential writer then living, came to Kapitsa's rescue. In 1921, thanks to Gorky's intercession, as well as Ioffe's recommendation, a visa was granted to Kapitsa.

The official fiction was that the Academy of Sciences was sending him abroad as a member of a professorial delegation to renew contacts with foreign scholars, also to purchase sorely needed books and laboratory equipment. Shabbily dressed, thin, thoughtful, he sailed for London.

III

His reputation had preceded him. A few British scientists somehow knew of Peter Kapitsa as a brilliant blend of powerful analyst and practical engineer. Lord Rutherford at once made a place for Peter in his famous Cavendish Laboratory at Cambridge. (However, later Kapitsa would say that at the time no one in England knew him.)

Lord Rutherford was the genius who discovered the nucleus of the atom and was the first to change the structure of an atom. But other problems of physics were also being researched at his laboratory. Kapitsa was in time recognized as the Old Wizard's favorite staff member. Under Rutherford's guidance, although never working with him on any common project, Kapitsa busied himself with the investigation of the reaction of matter to the influence of magnetic fields. His spirits soon revived; he was now increasingly confident and even gay.

Peter Kapitsa: The Man and His Work

Yet, a few scientists did not exactly like Kapitsa—for reasons both personal and political. Among these men were his fellow Russian émigrés. They were definitely (and some belligerently) anti-Soviet, but young Kapitsa seemed equivocal at best. To some acquaintances he explained himself as not an émigré but an emissary, that is, a scientist still on a Moscow mission of research and purchase of equipment and books, with a vaguely acknowledged obligation someday to return home to the Soviets.

Professor Stepan Timoshenko, an émigré already then making a great name for himself in American academic and engineering circles for his work in theoretical and applied mechanics, met Kapitsa at a scientific congress in Edinburgh in September 1921. Years later he recalled that even in his first few months at Cambridge young Kapitsa "felt no lack of any of his necessities," because "the Bolshevik government furnished him with money fairly generously." It was this money, Timoshenko went on, that indirectly helped Kapitsa gain initial fame of a sort in England.

He could even afford to buy a motorcycle. On this he began experimenting. He wanted to ascertain the utmost speed that could be attained on it. These experiments ended for him badly. On one occasion, while making a turn at high speed, the motorcycle crashed, and Kapitsa found himself in a ditch. The impact was considerable, but his arms and legs survived intact. His face and chest, however, did suffer. Someone picked Kapitsa up and delivered him to a hospital, where he had to remain for more than a week.

Telling of this adventure the very first evening of his meeting with Timoshenko at Edinburgh, Kapitsa related that in the hospital he "was bored waiting for a full recovery and so, his head still bandaged, went back to the laboratory." The effect was dramatic. One after another his associates came to Kapitsa's cubicle, asked questions in awe, and wished him to get well soon. "Finally Rutherford himself made his appearance,

5

gazed at the bandaged head, and left silently. This made Kapitsa rather well known in the laboratory."

Grudgingly Timoshenko admitted that at the scientific congress in Edinburgh, at the university's dormitory where the visiting scientists were housed, the young and exuberant Kapitsa quickly proved himself to be as popular as apparently he had become at Cambridge.

In the evening, when all gathered in the drawing room, he amused the public by his tricks and experiments. He was extraordinarily bold. When, in the course of an experiment, he needed an assistant, he would unceremoniously pull some celebrated scientist by his sleeve and begin to explain to him just what it was he had to do. Solemn, dignified Englishmen lost their gravity of manner and fully submitted to Kapitsa's decisive actions.[5]

I V

Some of Kapitsa's audacity may have come from his inner conviction that he had something of value to offer to these British and their society. Indeed, he did. As even Timoshenko allowed, "his superiority over young English scientists came from his passage through the excellent engineering school of the St. Petersburg Polytechnic Institute." He therefore could and did design large machinery. "In his scientific work he tended to shift from small physics equipment to big machines, and this change of the experiment's scale gave him a chance to carry out a series of important researches."[6]

In 1923 Peter Kapitsa defended his dissertation and was awarded his doctorate by Cambridge. The same year brought him the James Clark Maxwell Prize, one of the world's highest scientific honors. In 1924 he developed unique equipment for work with superpowerful magnetic fields. More and more the eyes of Britain's scientists were upon him. In 1929 Kapitsa was elected to the Royal Society, the first foreigner (so it was said) to receive this honor in two centuries. By the early 1930s he had been elected also to the British Institute of Physics, to the Cambridge Philosophical Society, and to Trinity College. He was presently a full professor at Cambridge. The Royal Society built a special laboratory to suit his exacting specifications. In 1932 he designed a high-production hydrogen liquefier. In 1934 he began blueprints of his original apparatus for producing large quantities of liquid oxygen (further developed and constructed in 1938). His administrative posts included an assistant directorship in the Cavendish Magnetic Research Laboratory and, from 1930, a directorship in the Cambridge University Laboratory.

The mutual respect between Rutherford and Kapitsa grew into a close friendship. Already in 1923 the British master considered the young Russian an outstanding star of the Cavendish Laboratory, "one of the finest scientific brains which even that great nursery of talent had ever seen." [7] In early 1925 Rutherford wrote in a private letter to R. W. Boyle about Kapitsa's "big experiment for producing magnetic fields" and gave enthusiastic details:

> This research is being financed by the Government, and involves the installation in one of the old Engineering Laboratories of a complete power station with a 1500 kilowatt machine as the source of the power. It is a very elaborate experiment and I hope it will come off all right. If so, there will of course be a great deal of work to do in the examining of magnetic properties in these very high fields. The whole scheme will cost a good deal and will be financed by the Department of Scientific Research. [8]

On December 17, 1925, Kapitsa wrote from the Cavendish Laboratory to Rutherford, then traveling for pleasure:

> I am writing you this letter to Cairo to tell you that we already have the short circuit machine and the coil, and

we managed to obtain fields over 270,000 [units] in a cylindrical volume of a diameter of 1 cm, and 4½ cms high. We could not go further as the coil bursted with a great bang, which, no doubt, would amuse you very much, if you could hear it.

. . . .

At present all these experiments have been done with a higher speed machine, and I am very happy that everything went well, and now you may be quite sure 98 per cent of the money is not wasted, and everything is working.

The accident was the most interesting of all the experiments, and gives the final touch of certainty, as we now know exactly what has happened when the coil bursted. . . . I am very impatient to see you again in the laboratory and to tell you all the little details, some of which are amusing, about the fight with the machines. . . .[9]

On February 3, 1933, the new Royal Society Mond Laboratory was officially opened at the University of Cambridge by Prime Minister Stanley Baldwin, then also the University's Chancellor. The money came from the Ludwig Mond Bequest to the Royal Society, and the laboratory was meant mainly for the development of physics of the advanced type in which Kapitsa was pioneering. The Mond Laboratory was to be actually within the Cavendish Laboratory complex, semi-independent but under Rutherford's supervision. On the main door of the Mond Laboratory a picture of a crocodile was carved at Kapitsa's request, in Rutherford's honor, he said. He called Rutherford *krokodil* "as a symbol of Rutherford's scientific acumen and career," because "this animal never turns back" but always pushes forward; "the crocodile is regarded in Russia with mingled awe and admiration."[10]

In his personal life Kapitsa was also finding increased stability and happiness; in 1929, in London, Anna Krylova became his second wife. She was the daughter of Professor Aleksei

Krylov. In the early 1930s she bore Peter Kapitsa two children.

Kapitsa's father-in-law was a prominent mathematician, physicist, astronomer, and above all a first-rate shipbuilder.[11] While at first in his British residence Kapitsa appeared to be on a Soviet mission but later ceased this connection and became in effect a Russian expatriate, Krylov was never an émigré. Krylov's years in England, 1921-27, were spent clearly on a mission for the Soviet government: he supervised the building of ships ordered in England by the Soviets and carried out other technical assignments from Moscow. True, he felt independent enough to meet, and eat and drink, with those of his prerevolutionary Russian friends and associates who were now émigrés in London and Paris; he listened to their anti-Soviet talk, but he was most careful and reserved on any problem involving Russian politics. "Krylov had to return [to the Soviet Union]; therefore he had to be cautious," wrote Professor Timoshenko.[12]

Krylov was destined to play an important role in Kapitsa's eventual fate. But there are two different—in fact, diametrically opposite—reports on the nature of that role.

V

It was in the late 1920s and early '30s that the Soviet government intensified its bold, smart campaign of enticing gifted émigrés back into Russia. Stalin wanted certain key men of the arts and sciences to return. His agents—or just nostalgia—had already won several successes. Among the willing returnees were the composer Sergei Prokofiev, and the writers Maxim Gorky, Aleksei Tolstoy, and Ilya Ehrenburg. Some who were sent abroad on missions could have stayed as émigrés but did not. Among such returnees was Professor Krylov, Anna Kapitsa's father.

And now for Kapitsa. As Peter's renown became world-wide, Stalin and his men realized his worth. They now knew that in letting Kapitsa go abroad a grievous error had been made. Two items were just then discovered by Soviet intelligence men in England.

Item One. Anna Kapitsa missed her father. And as her father's letters began to arrive from Russia, she found that she longed also for one more look at her homeland.

Item Two. Nominally, Peter Kapitsa was still a Soviet citizen. He was refusing all offers of the British government to make him His Majesty's subject.

Why was he shunning British citizenship? Was he now pro-Soviet? No. He was merely a patriot of his old fatherland without any love or respect for the government that happened to be ruling it. He felt it was his duty to return to Russia someday for good—to give to his people the benefit of his talent and knowledge.

Someday, but not too soon. This much was plain from Kapitsa's remarks to his friends on the subject of the Soviets. He would return permanently only if and when there was freedom in Russia.

The Kremlin heard of this, but was still hopeful. In 1933, cautiously, cleverly, the Kremlin let out feelers. Would the prodigal son return just for a visit? A scientific congress was to meet next year in Moscow, surely of much interest to Kapitsa. The congress was to honor the memory of Dmitry Mendeleyev, the great Russian chemist, on the centennial of his birth. Also it was known that Kapitsa needed a rest. He could, when the congress was over, take his vacation in the Crimea and the Caucasus instead of the French Riviera. He could bring Anna and his car along, drive anywhere in Russia, then leave for abroad again. His Russian colleagues, from his old teacher Ioffe down to the greenest assistants in Soviet physics, were yearning for a talk with him. Stalin himself gave his word to let Kapitsa out once the visit was completed. Now, would Kapitsa come for a while, a brief while?

Kapitsa shook his head. But Anna pressed, Anna implored. And Peter gave in. Reluctantly, but he did. A Russian émigré, Boris Nicolaevsky, wrote to me about this moment in the

Kapitsas' life: "She greatly longed for her native land. . . . Kapitsa himself was very reluctant to go—I know this from his close friends." [13]

V I

Such was one report, one belief, widely current among the Russian émigrés in Western Europe and the United States. But another story, at sharp variance with the preceding, was known less generally, and chiefly to those who were scientists and well acquainted with Kapitsa or at least with his activities.

This second story had it that all through the 1920s Kapitsa went on periodic trips to the Soviet Union and returned to England with no hindrance from the Soviets at all. Kapitsa himself confirmed this when in May 1966, in his address before the Royal Society of London, he spoke of going to the Soviet Union in 1934 "as was my custom." A detailed account of Kapitsa's repeated journeys to his native land in the 1920s was given by Professor Timoshenko in his book of 1963. To turn to Timoshenko's reminiscences:

In July 1926, on a trip to Cambridge, Professor Timoshenko was entertained by Kapitsa "most graciously," as the rather hostile guest conceded.

He was on the Trinity College staff and had his lodgings right opposite the main gate of that College. To honor my arrival Kapitsa arranged in his flat a tea, to which he invited several young physicists. Kapitsa loved to talk. He told many tales about his trips to Russia, whither he was repeatedly invited to lecture about the development of physics in England. But he was not too burdened by such lectures, and he spent most of his time at Kislovodsk [a resort in the Northern Caucasus]. Now he was talking about his latest trip, during which he had managed to visit his old family home, somewhere in the Volyn province. At that he had succeeded in carrying out with him a few items of his family's silver, and here he pointed to the tea set standing before us.

But Professor Timoshenko did not believe Kapitsa. ". . . I thought to myself that he had been given this set out of the 'cigarette-case fund' * as compensation for his lectures." [14]

Toward the end of that summer of 1926, while in Paris, Timoshenko ran into Krylov, Kapitsa's father-in-law, on the street. They had dinner in the company of some fellow Russians, and Krylov told Timoshenko that he would like to see him soon alone, on a private matter. Several days later, Timoshenko called on Krylov at his hotel. The matter, it turned out, concerned Kapitsa. "Krylov asked me to warn Kapitsa to decline any further invitations from Russia. . . . At my very next meeting with Kapitsa I told him of this warning, but he paid little attention to it." [15]

Timoshenko saw Kapitsa for the last time in the summer of 1934, at a scientific congress held at Cambridge. Despite his dislike of Kapitsa, he was impressed by the physicist's successes in England. Once more Timoshenko explained this triumph by Kapitsa's old Russian schooling: "Physics, in its development, demanded large-scale, factory-size experimentation, and Kapitsa, with the engineering education he brought from the St. Petersburg Polytechnic Institute, had considerable advantage over the theoreticians of the university type." The two talked about Russia again.

> Kapitsa told me that during his years at Cambridge he had been repeatedly invited to Soviet Russia for reports and lectures, and that he found such trips most interesting, since following the reports and lectures it was very pleasant to spend the remainder of a summer somewhere in the Crimea or the Caucasus. I remarked that such journeys were not without their dangers; it was quite possible that

* This expression, "the cigarette-case fund," was then common among Russians both at home and abroad to denote the valuables confiscated by the Communists, in 1917 and later, from the upper- and middle-class persons in Russia, in many instances before or after their execution by firing squads.

one beautiful day the Soviet government might detain him, and he would never return to England. But he only laughed. Such a turn of affairs seemed improbable to him.[16]

Apparently, in returning to Russia in 1934 reluctantly or not, Kapitsa trusted Stalin's word. Why did he?

Some who knew him at the time recall that Maxim Gorky backed Stalin's promise with his own guarantee. Gorky swore to see to it that Kapitsa was not stopped from leaving Russia when ready to go. And Kapitsa believed Gorky, because Gorky had secured for Kapitsa his original exit visa in 1921. And in 1934 Gorky was even more powerful than he had been thirteen years before. Stalin now openly deferred to Gorky (while secretly plotting Gorky's death, by poison, which came in 1936).

Thus it was, in the early fall of 1934, that Kapitsa returned to Russia, an Englishman perhaps more than a Russian. His friend Niels Bohr, the Danish atomic physicist, accompanied Peter and Anna.

V I I

In Russia, Kapitsa looked around with shrewd eyes. He saw that his old homeland was immeasurably stronger and far more orderly than when he had first left it. He was impressed by certain improvements introduced by the Soviets. He was pleased when he re-examined the scenes of his childhood and youth and again when—after parting with Bohr, who sailed back to Denmark—he and Anna drove in their car southward, to their beloved Crimea and Caucasus.

But though he and Anna were free in their movements, he noticed that not many Russians were. His early disapproval of things Soviet was confirmed. By the end of several weeks he dreamed of his adopted England, his Cambridge, with its freedom and decency. Naturally both he and Anna missed their children. And so the two turned back.

They drove north to Leningrad to supervise the loading of

13

their car and of sundry souvenirs onto a Britain-bound steamer. It was here that the Kapitsas were told:

"Your exit visas have been canceled."

They were stunned. Their worst fears had come true. Peter argued. In vain. He and Anna had to turn back to Moscow.

In Moscow, high officials were poker-faced. Sorry, but Professor Kapitsa was a Soviet citizen and had to stay. His country needed him. Great things were in store for him. He would have everything—even his Mond Laboratory at Cambridge. Yes, Stalin ordered that, if possible, the entire laboratory in Cambridge should be purchased for him and brought to Moscow. What would the professor say to this?

The professor said no. And no, no, no—emphatically, again and again.

The officials shrugged their shoulders. They were polite. In contrast to the usual methods of the Soviet police, no force would be used on the great scientist. Give him time, and he would see the light. Such were the Kremlin's special orders. Stalin was patient.

The professor tried to outwait the dictator. For a whole year Peter and Anna Kapitsa lived in their hotel room, hardly stirring except for a walk, refusing to say yes, demanding their right to return to England.

Lord Rutherford and other foreign friends of Kapitsa addressed the Kremlin with protest and plea. Stalin hardly bothered to reply. The official Soviet answer was "that of course England would like to have Kapitsa, and that they, for their part, would equally like to have Rutherford in Russia!" In other words, England had as little right to claim Kapitsa the Russian for her own as Russia would have to demand Rutherford the Englishman for her laboratories. Four years later Professor A. S. Eve, the official biographer of Rutherford, appraised this Moscow view as a "sagacious and fair retort." [17]

Rutherford continued trying for a while, nonetheless. He attempted to engage Stanley Baldwin's aid, writing to him on April 29, 1935: "Kapitsa was commandeered as the Soviet authorities thought he was able to give important help to the electrical industry and they have not found out that they were misinformed." [18]

But Stalin knew perfectly well that Kapitsa was a scientist no less than an engineer. He was going to use Kapitsa in both capacities.

To Kapitsa, Stalin sent word that he would see him if the professor was in a more placable mood and wanted to talk things over.

In time Kapitsa weakened. He discovered that he longed for his work even more than for England. He would see Stalin. And so the two met and came to an agreement.

Things began to hum. Stalin's new promise was kept. Not sparing the expense, the Soviet government bought and brought to Moscow certain items of equipment in the Mond Laboratory—the items which had been used by Kapitsa for producing high magnetic fields. Rutherford helped in these negotiations most effectively. The British sold these items in the interests of science, since no one else but Kapitsa could use this equipment anyway, and since the money received for it went to buy England's first cyclotron. The exact British rationale and procedure, in the words of Rutherford's official biographer, were as follows:

> Since Mahomet could not go to the mountain, the mountain had to go to Mahomet. Negotiations were begun and Professors Adrian and Dirac went to Russia to interview Kapitsa and others. Finally the Russian Government bought the apparatus for £30,000—a fair and proper price —and Cockcroft had the apparatus packed and dispatched to Russia.
>
> Not all this money came to the Cavendish Laboratory, because the British Government, through the Department of Scientific and Industrial Research, had contributed large sums for the generator and other apparatus. It was agreed that the Cavendish would not compete with Kapitsa in his field of research, and the money received was devoted to other objects, in the Royal Society Mond Laboratory.[19]

But in time to come Kapitsa was to insist that he did not have a laboratory of his own for the first three or four years after his forcible detention in the Soviet Union in the fall of 1934. The negotiations for the Mond Laboratory equipment may have indeed taken at least two years, and the shipment and installation of the apparatus in its new place in Moscow another year or two.

Much else was done by Stalin for his captive. In 1935 Kapitsa was made director of the Institute of Problems of Physics, within the network of the Soviet Academy of Sciences. A corresponding member of the Academy from his British days (since 1929), he became a full-fledged member of the Academy in 1939.

Yet, it was not atomic physics that held Kapitsa's primary attention once he resumed his work. From 1935 on, his major achievements were in low temperatures and their application in the liquefying of air. To his credit he added the first discovery and investigation of hyperfluidity of liquid helium. His small, inexpensive turbine, used to take oxygen out of air, brought him a United States patent as well as new Kremlin honors.

An enthusiastic, devoted circle of colleagues and students formed around him at the Institute in Moscow. His Wednesday evening at-homes became a celebrated colloquium for years and years.

The two Kapitsa children were in time brought from England to rejoin their parents. The Harris tweeds which Kapitsa liked so well were ordered for him. Even the precise brand of Kapitsa's favorite English tobacco was imported for his pipe.

Nonetheless, for a long time he continued to brood, for he missed England, and in particular Rutherford, so much. Until the very end of Rutherford's life which was to come in just a few years, the British scientist wrote encouraging letters to Kapitsa at least once every two months. Kapitsa tried to respond with a kind of Russian fatalism. In 1936 he wrote to Rutherford: "After all, we are only small particles of floating matter in a stream which we call Fate. All that we can manage is to deflect slightly our track and keep afloat—the stream governs us!" [20] Rutherford's death on October 19, 1937, left Kapitsa with a great sense of personal bereavement.

Meanwhile, in Kapitsa's native land, clouds were gathering, thickening, threatening. The purges of the middle and latter 1930s struck Russia in a long, agonizing series. Most of the men and women who had ever had any dealings with the West were arrested and shot, or deported to concentration camps and slower death, by the hundreds, by the thousands. All around Peter Kapitsa friends, associates, acquaintances were dragged out of their homes and laboratories to a fate known or unknown. The secret police moved closer and closer to the physicist.

Among others Lev Landau, a rising Russian star of physics and mathematics, was arrested. A Jew, he was nevertheless accused of pro-Nazi activities. Nearly three decades later, in 1964 (two years after he was awarded a Nobel Prize), Landau recalled: "They charged me with being a German spy. Now, occasionally, this seems amusing to me, but at that time, believe me, I did not feel like laughing. I spent one year in prison, and it was clear to me that I wouldn't last another six months. I was dying, simply dying." It was Peter Kapitsa who finally saved him.

Kapitsa went to the Kremlin and . . . demanded my freedom. Otherwise, he said, he would leave his Institute. I was freed. It is hardly necessary to say that in those years, for such an act, one had to have great courage, great humanity, and crystal-clear honesty.[21]

VIII

In the early 1940s Kapitsa returned to the atomic field by helping other Soviet scientists in their nuclear researches. He built new instruments for the cosmic-ray observations carried on in the high mountains of the Pamirs and Soviet Armenia by the two Armenian brothers, Abram and Artemy Alikhanov.

During the war Kapitsa experimented with uranium and lectured on atomic physics in Moscow's military academies.

And yet the atom didn't seem to be his chief concern. When
in April 1944 the Franklin Institute of Philadelphia awarded
him the Franklin Medal, it was for his nonatomic work. For his
discovery of hyperfluidity he received the First Class Stalin
Prize twice, in 1941 and 1943. Early in 1945, when the Kremlin
gave Kapitsa the title of Hero of Socialist Labor, it was for
his researches into the turbine methods of oxygen production.

By 1946 he had the Order of Lenin, the highest award in the
Soviet scale of honors. At this time, in 1945-46, he smilingly
denied to foreign correspondents that he was under any dur-
ess. Urbane and relaxed, puffing on his briar, he spoke in his
colloquial English of all the facilities and honors he was enjoying in the land of the Soviets. In his public speeches he
dwelt at length on the glories of the U.S.S.R. Nevertheless,
rumors spread that Stalin was not too pleased with Kapitsa.

Stalin was rewarding him constantly, but more in hopes of
spurring Kapitsa on to atomic discoveries than in recognition
of work already done. Hints were carried to Kapitsa from the
Kremlin: move "closer to actual life" (as the common Russian
phrase had it)—that is, to the post-Hiroshima reality.

On the news of Hiroshima, Stalin had tripled the salaries of
his atomic scientists. As late as December 1945, Kapitsa bland-
ly revealed that his most recent work had been with hydrogen.
Unofficially, however, all the world had heard or guessed by
then that Kapitsa was leading the entire effort to produce a
Soviet A-bomb. Norbert Wiener, who had known him at Cambridge in the early 1930s, said later that he was not surprised.
He recalled that in Russia, Kapitsa "became the pioneer of
that large-scale, factorylike type of laboratory which had first
been employed by [Heike] Kamerlingh Onnes in the Nether-
lands for low-temperature research, and which is now the
standard means of exploring the nucleus and of designing
atomic bombs." In 1945, just as soon as Wiener had first heard
of the American atom bomb, he felt sure that, with Kapitsa
training

the Russians in the technique of this sort of laboratory, it would not be many years before they would have mastered for themselves the principles and techniques of nuclear research, whether or not they might capture our secrets by means of espionage or persuade a group of malcontents to serve their purposes.[22]

In the summer of 1946, to Richard E. Lauterbach, a young American journalist who questioned him about the atom bomb, Kapitsa made a wry face. "To talk of atomic energy in terms of the atomic bomb," he said, "is like talking of electricity in terms of the electric chair." [23]

A man of peace, Kapitsa was hoping for an international agreement to outlaw the atomic bomb. He hoped for mankind's survival. But, increasingly, he criticized the Americans for what he termed unnecessary stubbornness in safeguarding atomic secrets.

This is where the new mystery of Kapitsa began. Was he sincere in this criticism? Did he gradually allow himself to be convinced by Stalin's men that we were being perverse in not destroying our stocks of A-bombs as the Kremlin wished us to do, and that as a Russian patriot he must do his best for the Soviet version of the A-bomb? Or was he only *talking* like a loyal Stalinist—to cover up his possible decision *not* to lead the Soviet atomic race against the West?

The mystery deepened when suddenly, late in 1946, Kapitsa's name vanished from official Soviet news. He was no longer head of the Institute of Problems of Physics nor in the lists of Russian atomic scientists awarded Stalin's prizes and medals. No letter from him or about him reached foreign parts. Complete official silence surrounded Kapitsa.

Two long years passed, and then, in 1948, an article of his appeared in a Soviet journal of experimental and theoretical physics. In February 1949, another article by Kapitsa was printed in the official annals of the Soviet Academy of Sciences. But neither was on atomics—both were on liquids.

Was Kapitsa being *zasekrechen*—that is, surrounded by ut-

19

most secrecy and security—because of astounding successes in atomics since late 1946? Or, on the contrary, was he being punished by Stalin because he either couldn't or wouldn't help the Kremlin's efforts to produce an A-bomb? All sorts of reports circulated then, and still abound now, about this period in Kapitsa's colorful life, but the most authentic facts seem to be these:

In Stalin's final years Kapitsa refused to contribute his genius to the evolvement or improvement of the Soviet atomic and hydrogen bombs. Stalin, not daring to shoot or even exile the great scientist, had him confined under house arrest, which may have lasted several years.

In his *Moscow Summer* Mihajlo Mihajlov, while reporting on his conversation with the celebrated Soviet writer Vladimir Tendryakov, noted: "Among other things, Tendryakov told us that his friend, the Academician Kapitsa, famous as a mathematical genius, was under house arrest for eight years during the Stalin era." [24] In early 1965 Ilya Ehrenburg revealed how dismayed Kapitsa's British friends had been on hearing of his arrest. At the end of Stalin's era, Ehrenburg was in England on a mission for the Soviet "peace" movement of the time. He was taken on a visit to Cambridge, where a distinguished physicist and his wife cautiously and unhappily inquired about Kapitsa's troubles. Ehrenburg tried to reassure them; he felt that his hosts "wanted to believe me but did not dare to." They were slightly reassured when Ehrenburg agreed to deliver their gift of a few skeins of wool to Anna Kapitsa (who loved to knit).[25]

That Kapitsa was indeed under house arrest for a period near the close of Stalin's era seems now indisputable, if only because mention of the arrest was later, in Khrushchev's time, allowed to seep through in foreign correspondents' dispatches from Moscow uncensored and unrefuted.

Peter Kapitsa returned to freedom and to the world's headlines soon after Stalin's death. In August 1953, when Russia's possession of an H-bomb of her own became known, Kapitsa's earlier role in this achievement was surmised. In Washington it was recalled that Kapitsa's particular specialty involved the major matter of the hydrogen bomb—the behavior of materials at very high and very low temperatures. Also recalled was a December 1945 statement by Kapitsa to the effect that he had transformed hydrogen into a hard, visible metal. The chairman of the United States Joint Committee on Atomic Energy once remarked, with disquiet, on Kapitsa's special competence in the technical problems relating to hydrogen weapons.

In 1955, two years after Stalin's death, Kapitsa was reinstated as director of the Institute of Problems of Physics. Also in 1955 he made public his hypothesis about the origin of ball lightning, which in some scientific quarters is seriously considered for its potential as a military weapon of tremendous force.

In July 1957 the British pacifist weekly *Peace News*, in a London-to-Moscow telephone interview, asked Kapitsa whether he had indeed refused to work on Soviet atomic and hydrogen bombs. Kapitsa's reply was, "Quite right," and he went on to reveal that "other Soviet scientists had taken a similar position." This was confirmed in September 1957 by Wilfred Burchett, an Australian Communist, as he described his own visit and interview with Kapitsa "in his palatial offices" in Moscow. He wrote that Kapitsa said to him: "I have never worked on bombs." [26]

Even if Burchett can be trusted (which, in view of his record, is not too often), the year was 1957 and much has happened since then. It is quite possible that the Party now favors Kapitsa at least in part because the scientist has by this time changed his ideas about bombs that are too destructive: it is sometimes supposed in the West that currently Kapitsa supervises Soviet laboratories for development of atomic and hydrogen bombs and military use of cosmic-ray energy.

IX

And yet his rebellious voice is still raised. To cite an outstanding example:

21

Peter Kapitsa: The Man and His Work

Men of science and politics the world over sat up and took notice when on March 26, 1962, the Moscow *Ekonomicheskaya gazeta* printed Dr. Kapitsa's lengthy article "Theory, Experiment, Practice." [27] Therein the internationally famous physicist declared that without the science of cybernetics * Soviet outerspace successes would have been impossible. Yet, the scientist recalled, only some eight years earlier certain Soviet dogmatists had had the stupid nerve to denounce cybernetics as something capitalistic and thus worthless, unclean, harmful.

With dignified anger Dr. Kapitsa quoted *Filosofichesky slovar'* (Philosophical Dictionary), published in 1954, one year after Stalin's death, but still mirroring the official Stalinist negation of computing machines: "Cybernetics is a reactionary pseudo science, which emerged in the United States after World War II and spread widely in other capitalistic countries as well."

Seizing upon the title of the 1954 book, Professor Kapitsa berated its authors as "philosophers" who had made a "mistake" and who as philosophers should have foreseen the further development of natural sciences instead of pronouncing their rigid judgments on a past phase of these sciences.

Never once did he call them Stalinists, nor (of course) did he say that Khrushchev had been one of Stalin's top hatchet men, responsible directly or indirectly for that era's atrocities. Remarking merely that "this mistake has been corrected," Kapitsa went on to state that already in 1954, if not earlier, Russia's true scientists refused to bow to those Soviet "philosophers," and how lucky this was for the nation! He wrote:

Had our scientists at the time, in 1954, obeyed the philosophers, had they adopted this definition [of cybernetics] as their directive for the further development of this science, we can say that our conquest of outer space, of which all of us are justly proud and for which the entire world

* Cybernetics, the science of those methods of control and communication which are common to living organisms and machines, is used as a term—in Russian perhaps more widely than in Western languages—to cover also linear programming, information retrieval, servomechanisms, and other fields and features related to electronic computing.

22

respects us, could not have occurred, since it is impossible to guide a spaceship without cybernetic machines.

Nor would the Soviets have emerged with their own atomic bomb when they did, Kapitsa continued, had the Soviet "philosophers" been obeyed in their abuse of another science milestone: Albert Einstein's work on relativity. He pointed out that already in Einstein's time physicists had confirmed his theory by their experiments with atomic particles, but that Soviet dogmatists disregarded this evidence.

To understand such experiments a profound knowledge of the latest physics was needed, but certain philosophers lacked this knowledge. And by now physicists . . . have confirmed the Einstein law, not on separate atoms, but on the scale of the atom bomb. How embarrassed our physicists would have been had they followed those philosophers' conclusions and had they ceased their work on the problem of applying the theory of relativity in nuclear physics!

In his March 1962 article Kapitsa implied that way back in those days, in the 1940s and early '50s, he was among the bold ones who shrugged off the anti-Einstein mania and the anti-cybernetic dogma, who went on with their genuinely scientific work. Kapitsa's house arrest (or even direr punishment, if we are to believe certain more sinister reports) may have been caused not alone by his refusal to work on the atomic bomb. An additional cause may have been his disagreement with Stalin's "philosophers" on the validity of relativity and cybernetics.

X

Still, what exactly was behind Peter Kapitsa's sudden attack of 1962 on those Soviet dogmatists for their erstwhile sabotage of Einstein's ideas and computer work in Russia? Why his extraordinary review of this particular Stalinist sin, which, like all the other varieties of the late dictator's whims, was supposed to be safely dead by 1962?

Nine years after Stalin's demise, Einstein and computers were at last raised from the limbo of taboo or official neglect by the Communists. Computers in fact were being worshiped all over the Soviet scene. The Party's new program, adopted at the Twenty-second Congress in Moscow in October 1961, proudly trumpeted that for the next two decades the widest possible use would be made of computing, control, and information machines. Why, then, the outburst by Dr. Kapitsa—the seemingly belated broadside against those Stalinist dogmatists? Was it merely historical, a proud and near-gloating reminiscence of that horrid period's sufferings as a prelude to the latter-day triumphs of true scientists?

Not entirely and not primarily. Professor Kapitsa made it clear that the present and the future of Soviet science and politics were involved no less than their past. Interference in Soviet science by Communist politicians continued, he hinted in his March 1962 manifesto. He sideswiped Trofim Lysenko, the leader of Soviet antigeneticists, without naming him, yet plainly meaning him when he wrote about "the incorrect generalizations made by our philosophers, not only in the field of physics, but also in the field of biology."

Kapitsa then proceeded to his main target, which was none other than the old sacred cow of Marxism: dialectical materialism. He wrote in his "Theory, Experiment, Practice" cautiously, yet unmistakably:

> . . . Application of dialectics in the realm of natural sciences demands an exceptionally thorough knowledge of experimental facts and their theoretical generalization. Without this, dialectics by itself cannot solve the question. Dialectics is like a Stradivarius violin. To play this most perfect of all violins, one must be a musician and know music. Without this, it would yield false notes just as an ordinary fiddle would.

Somehow he seemed to connect the dogmatists' misuse of

dialectics with the fact that young Soviet physicists shunned experimentation. Too little experimentation was being done in the Soviet Union even in the early 1960s, Professor Kapitsa asserted in his significant article. In this lag he saw a danger signal for the future of Soviet science. He explained; he cited facts and figures: as editor of the journal *Eksperimental'naya i teoreticheskaya fizika* [28] he noted that, in the themes of articles submitted to him, theoretical physics outnumbered experimental physics three and even four to one. For various reasons, "young Soviet college graduates . . . want theoretical, not experimental, work as their specialty," he pointed out. He warned: "We cannot permit any lag in experimental physics, for this would greatly hinder the normal growth of our physics —would prevent it from occupying leading positions in the world's science along the entire front of most important researches."

While some of the reasons for the young Soviet researchers' reluctance had nothing to do with politics, others did. Professor Kapitsa intimated that fear of Marxist dialectics was among the handicaps to experimentation in the Soviet Union. In sum, he blamed the Soviet "philosophers," who, although less pernicious than they had been in Stalin's time, were still strong enough to oppose true science.

But were there any true philosophers in the Soviet Union in 1962? Was Dr. Kapitsa's outburst aimed not at any genuine philosophers, but rather, in fact, at those Communist Party officials and their Lysenko-like sycophants who may have still been trying to run Russia's science in a stifling, would-be Marxist way?

X I

In the early and middle 1960s Kapitsa also added his weighty voice to the defense of experimenters in the Soviet arts.

Khrushchev's campaign against the modern tendencies in Russia's art reached its peak in December 1962, when Khrushchev summoned to a glass-walled reception palace in Moscow's Lenin Hills a group of top-ranking writers, painters, and sculptors to harangue them on their sins. Courageously they talked back, and the argument stormed for five hours. One of the most interesting points of the debate was the answer given by Ernest Neizvestny, the well-known abstract sculptor, to Khrushchev's abuse of him: "You may not like my work, Comrade Khrushchev, but it has the warm admiration of such eminent Soviet scientists as Kapitsa and Landau." Khrushchev countered with scorn: "That's not why we admire Kapitsa and Landau." [29] Apparently he did not realize how much beside the point his answer was.

In the summer of 1965, during his trip to Kazan on the Volga to attend a conference of physicists, Kapitsa met a young experimenting painter, Aleksei Anikeyonok. He was fascinated by the artist's imaginative style and creative integrity. He brought him and his canvases to Moscow. The officials in charge of Soviet art condemned Anikeyonok as a "bourgeois formalist." Calmly Kapitsa faced their ire as he personally arranged a show for the rebel in the halls of the Institute of Problems of Physics.[30]

In December 1964, in a speech subsequently published in an Academy journal, Kapitsa called for greater freedom for Soviet scientists when he said that, although they could get money for their research more easily than their American colleagues could, the governmental restrictions made Soviet research less productive. Let us emulate some of the American practices, he urged. Availability of able researchers, rather than the attraction of this field or that to the government, should be the guiding principle. Give funds to those who can use them fruitfully, not to those in an area of research which may be judged important by the authorities but which may lack truly capable scientists.[31]

At about the same time, in April 1965, in an oblique but again unmistakable way, he demanded freer travel abroad for those Soviet scholars who really needed it, among them himself. He made this demand clear in his article commemorating the two-hundredth anniversary of Mikhail Lomonosov's death, wherein he praised "the . . . international friendship of scientists" and pointed out: "Nowadays the necessity of personal contacts among scientists is taken for granted by our and foreign savants." [32]

This was doubtless to call the world's attention to the fact that ever since 1934 he, Peter Kapitsa, had not once been allowed to go abroad. And it was to ensure the Soviet government's permission for him to travel to Denmark the very next month, in May 1965, when he was to receive the Neils Bohr International Gold Medal awarded to him by the Danish Engineering Society for his work in the peaceful uses of atomic energy.

On May 23, for the first time in thirty-one years, Kapitsa left Soviet soil—to receive the medal from the hands of King Frederick IX, to tour Danish laboratories, and to deliver a lecture in Copenhagen on high-energy physics.[33]

Finally, in the spring of the following year, he revisited his beloved England. He found his old Cambridge house (which, according to one report, he had kept in ownership all these thirty-two years of absence); he walked through the Cavendish and Mond Laboratories with a considerable heart tug, no doubt; he greeted the few old friends who were still alive. On May 4, as he faced journalists at a Royal Society news conference, he calmly jested about the surest way to bring peace on earth: "Arrange an exchange of scientists from military institutions. Then there would be no more secrets." He regretted the American drain of British scientists, but said it was not a Russian problem: "Because we have nobody to drain." When asked whether in 1934, on his detention by Stalin, he had felt scientifically isolated, he quizzically remarked that this was "a romantic question." [34] On May 17 he addressed the Royal Society with his reminiscences of Rutherford.

And then of course he returned home to Moscow. For he still had much work to do in Russia. In his mid-seventies, Peter Kapitsa is still the faithful sentinel of non-Marxist science in the Soviet Union. Blue-eyed, tweedy, ever puffing on his English pipe, now animated and now calm, he is indeed the aging yet very much living conscience of those ever-growing and increasingly stirring Soviet laboratories and lecture halls.

Through the darkest era of Stalinism he preserved at least a spark of the scientist's independence. In the easier post-Stalinist years he has served as a rallying point of resistance to the political bosses and their deadly doctrine. Thanks in a large measure to him, younger men now can carry on with a yet bolder course of scholar's freedom.

ALBERT PARRY

Colgate University

Note: The above Introduction is an expanded and revised version of Chapter III, "Peter Kapitsa: Symbol of Resistance," in Albert Parry, *The New Class Divided: Science and Technology Versus Communism* (New York: The Macmillan Company, 1966), pp. 27–45.

I

FOUR MEN
OF SCIENCE

1

Franklin's Scientific Activity

[*This address on Benjamin Franklin (1706-1790) was delivered
by Dr. Kapitsa on the occasion of the 250th anniversary of
Franklin's birth, celebrated at a special session of the Soviet
Academy of Sciences held at Moscow University on January
17, 1956.*]

Franklin was born in America, in the city of Boston, in 1706.
He died at the age of eighty-four. His activity spanned practically all of the eighteenth century and was closely tied with the
rapid development, then occurring, of the natural and social
sciences. This was an epoch of enlightenment, preceding the
period of radical social changes in Europe.

Franklin became part of the history of the world's culture
not alone as a great scientist, one of the founders of study of
electricity, but also as a great statesman and civic leader of
America who stood for progress, who took a most active part
in the struggle to free that country from its status as a colony.

His contemporaries were unanimous in describing Franklin
as a man of exceptional charm, an interesting, sharp-witted

conversationalist, well educated in all fields, and holding broadly humane views. Franklin traveled much and lived a-broad many years, particularly in England and France, where he was close to the leading personalities of his time. Toward his life's end he became Europe's most popular man.

To this day, in his native America, Franklin remains one of the most respected names since the beginning of the history of the United States.

Franklin's many-faceted life and work are well researched and known; a number of books have been written about him.

Franklin's basic scientific discoveries in the field of electricity date back to the 1750s, preceding Galvani's and Volta's work, that is, prior to the epoch of the galvanic current. Franklin's discoveries thus belong to the initial period of the conquest, by science, of this powerful force of nature.

In the two hundred years elapsing since Franklin's work, the study of electricity has progressed so much that nowadays Franklin's contribution is studied in secondary schools, in those courses where an acquaintance with physics is just begun. All of us, from our young years on, know the fundamentals of man's study of static electricity, even though some of us may have possibly forgotten precisely what constituted Franklin's contribution in this field. For instance, do all of us remember that it was Franklin to whom science is indebted for his introduction of the terminology of the positive and negative currents?

A detailed description of Franklin's scientific labors would hardly be of interest now. Yet it seems to me that the very history of the stage-by-stage progress of Franklin's work in the field of electricity is not only of interest but also of value to a modern scientist. And this is so because the road of the development of science, that is, the path taken by mankind in its learning of nature, should be just one road. In our search for scientific truth we often go off the right path, and thus time is wasted. Therefore, the less we deviate from the right way, the faster and the more economically our knowledge and conquest of nature's forces will develop. As we study the history of science, we find those factors which help a rapid progress of science. From this standpoint the history of Franklin's scientific researches is of an exceptional importance to us.

Franklin's work in electricity was carried out by him within a short period of time, in just seven years, from 1747 through 1753. He was already forty-one when he first began his scientific quest. By that time Franklin was a well-to-do man. Such enterprises as a printery, a newspaper, and a celebrated almanac, established by him in Philadelphia, then as yet a small town, were considerable successes. It was entirely by happenstance that Franklin started out on his scienfic bent. This was after he had chanced to attend a popular lecture which featured demonstrations in electricity. Such lectures were then frequent, since a number of electrical phenomena (repulsion and attraction of electrified bodies, the electric spark, and the unpleasant sensations caused by sending a discharge through a human), being at the time novel and wholly unusual, served as excellent material for popular lectures on science.

Shortly before he attended this lecture on electricity, the Leyden jar had been invented, which for the first time furnished a method of condensing electricity in an appreciable quantity. The opportunity to carry out experiments with a considerable reserve of electricity at once made demonstration of electrical phenomena that much more effective.

Franklin became greatly engrossed in electrical experimentation; for seven years he devoted most of his time to scientific work. This work at that time undoubtedly proved to be of major significance in the development of the study of electricity and won world-wide recognition. In this short period Franklin was acclaimed as a top-ranking scientist of his era. Most of that period's important scientific societies or academies hailed Franklin's scientific merit, electing him to membership, while a number of universities awarded him the honorary degree of doctor.

This question naturally arises: how could it happen that Franklin, never before working in physics, living so far away, in a small American town removed from the world's centers of science, a man already well along in years, succeeded within a few years of work in heading an entire discipline of science?

And this, mind you, occurred in the middle of the eighteenth century, when scientific endeavor was carried on by men at the level of knowledge of such savants as Newton, Huyghens,[1] and Euler.[2] No dilettantism here, surely. Well, then, how could Franklin achieve results of a kind that had been impossible for professional scientists to accomplish?

I think the explanation lies in the fact that Franklin was the first man to understand correctly the essence of electrical phenomena and therefore discovered the right path for further researches in this field. A similarly sharp turn in the development of the study of radioactivity, this tremendous and most important field of physics, happened in our days right before the eyes of many of us.

It was in 1896 that Becquerel[3] discovered the phenomenon of radioactivity. For years afterward scientists accumulated a wealth of experimental data as they studied physical phenomena connected with the radioactive property of matter. There was no order in all this variety of experimental data—inasmuch as the essence of the phenomenon of radioactivity was not understood. Rutherford was the first to find that physical phenomena connected with radioactivity have their immediate explanation if we are to suppose that radioactivity is a process of disintegration of matter. To perceive this, Rutherford did not need any profound erudition. The main thing necessary was his great imagination, perspicacity, and daring. In such initial phases of the development of a science, the precision and punctuality usual in professional scientists may rather hamper the postulation of daring premises of this kind.

In the initial stage of the study of electricity it was necessary that such a bold step be made. And Franklin made it.

Until Franklin's work made its appearance, a large quantity of experimental data had been gathered, but the facts had been separate from one another. The hypothesis offered by him not only united these facts into one harmonious picture but also showed the right path for further researches.

34

Franklin's Scientific Activity

Franklin laid down his basic hypothesis in a letter to Peter Collinson in 1749. The hypothesis gives a clear picture of the processes occurring during the electrization of bodies. To this day, in its essence, this picture remains correct. In his letter he wrote that the electrical matter consisted of extremely small particles, since they could penetrate ordinary things, as solid as metal, with such ease and freedom that they did not experience any appreciable resistance. These days our name for these "extremely small particles" is electrons. Further, Franklin regarded any body as if it were a sponge filled with these particles of electricity. The electrization of bodies is a state wherein a body having an excess of electrical particles is charged positively. Should a body be short of these particles, it is charged negatively. Quantitatively, Franklin proved this by a very graphic experiment.

Let us imagine that two persons stand on cushions made of wax, that is, on insulators. One of the men electrifies a little stick of glass by rubbing it. Then, should he touch the other individual with it, both are electrified in relation to the ground, and this is proved by the fact that either one of the two causes a spark if he touches an object on the ground. But should these men standing on insulators touch each other right after the electrification, a spark will fly between them, following which their electrification vis-à-vis the ground will disappear. And this is proved by the fact that no spark will be caused if they now touch a grounded object.

Franklin's hypothesis stemmed from the materialistic nature of electricity and simply explained these experiments. When an insulated man touches another insulated man with that little glass stick, one of the two loses electrical matter, and the other gains it to the very same extent. One of them is charged positively, the other negatively. If they touch each other, a discharge results, and insofar as the constant quantity of electrical matter is preserved, the prior balance is restored. Of course, Franklin at that time did not have an opportunity to understand through his experiment the material nature of electricity. He therefore had no opportunity to ascertain which one of the two persons received electrical matter and was thus charged positively and which one lost it, that is, which one was charged negatively. This was why Franklin presented it as his guess that electrified glass is charged positively, perhaps thinking that woolen material when rubbed against glass rubs electricity into it. Only at the end of the nineteenth century, after particles of electricity or electrons had been discovered, did it become known that a negative electrode, not a positive one as Franklin thought, collects electrical particles. In order not to change the symbols, by then so customary, of the positive and negative polarity, the negative charge was ascribed to the electron.

I will cite one more of Franklin's experiments, also of great scientific interest.

The feature of mutual repulsion by charged bodies of the same kind was extended by Franklin to charges contained in metal conductors. He considered that the charges, pushing away from each other, will strive to come to the outer part of the electrified metal body. He proved the correctness of his supposition by the following experiment.

A metal teakettle was placed on an insulator and was electrified. It was essential to find an experiment which would prove that the charge was distributed around the outside surface of the teakettle. For this purpose, inside the teakettle, a chain was placed, which could be—with the aid of an insulated handle—gradually drawn from the teakettle. The extent of the electrification of the teakettle was ascertained through the repulsion of two little balls, which were attached to the kettle by strings. The experiment was to lift the chain from the teakettle with the help of the insulated handle and to observe just how the kettle's electrification diminished as the chain was drawn out.

Franklin's reasoning was this: while the chain is inside the kettle, the chain's surface increases the interior surface of the kettle. As the chain is drawn out, it increases the exterior surface of the kettle. Franklin concluded: if the charge extends only along the exterior surface of the electrified conductor, this electrification will diminish only if the exterior surface is increased. And this is precisely what is observed during the ex-experiment.

I have cited these two experiments not only as works of genius in their simplicity, but also as most fundamental in their results.

A description of all his work was given by Franklin in his letters to his friend Collinson in England. In these letters we find descriptions of a large number of various experiments which by now are classic: obtaining an electric wind, properties of the flowing of charges from a sharp edge, and others. In the same letters Franklin gave, from the standpoint of his hypothesis, a correct explanation of a number of already known electrical phenomena, such as the piling up of electrical charges in the Leyden jar, and on this basis he made a flat condensator. Collinson reported on Franklin's work to the Royal Society. He later published these reports in a separate book, which became Franklin's main scientific volume. This book went through several editions and was translated into many languages.

I will not describe Franklin's other experiments except for those whereby he proved the electrical nature of lightning. These experiments became famous during Franklin's lifetime and brought him most of his renown. Although even before Franklin a hypothesis had been voiced that a bolt of lightning and a discharge resulting from electricity created by friction are one and the same phenomenon, even if of different scales, an experimental proof of the correctness of this hypothesis had been lacking.

The clarity and the correctness of Franklin's understanding of the phenomena of electrization gave him an opportunity to choose an experiment which for the first time proved convincingly the electrical nature of thunderstorm discharges. The idea of Franklin's experiment was as follows:

Let us suppose that there is placed, between a thunderstorm cloud and the ground, a long vertical metal rod, insulated from the ground. Should a thunderstorm cloud contain an electrical charge, the charge of the countersymbol is in the rod's upper part. If we make a sharp edge at the upper end of the rod, the guided charge will flow off, and the rod will be charged with electricity of the same symbol which is contained in the cloud.

Franklin thought that the presence of this charge will be revealed by the spark which results if the conductor is touched with the free end of a grounded wire. Franklin supposed, erroneously (as it became clear later), that for the experiment to succeed it was necessary to place the rod on an elevation, closer to the cloud. Since there was no such height close to his house, he thought he would not succeed with this experiment. He described in detail how this experiment should be carried out, suggesting that others undertake this. He himself decided to try an analogous experiment but in a somewhat different way that would not require an elevation.

For this experiment, instead of a metal rod, he decided to use a rope, raising it aloft by the means of a kite. Insofar as there is always a wind during a storm, the kite could be flown; and since there is also a rain, the rope will become wet and thus be a conductor, capable of substituting for a metal rod. For the rope to become charged more easily, a provision would be made for the guided charges to flow down from the upper end of the rope. For this purpose, Franklin placed sharp edges in the corners of the kite's frame. To insulate the rope from the ground, a silk ribbon was attached to the rope's lower part, and the ribbon was shielded from the rain. From the rope's end, near the ground, a metal key was suspended, and it was from this key that Franklin extracted a spark during the storm. In this way, in the presence of his friends and acquaintances, he proved the electrical nature of the storm's discharge. This experiment with the kite was done by Franklin on April 12, 1753, and it was then that he first found that thunder clouds as a rule are charged negatively.

Dalibard,[4] the French scientist, built at Marly-la-Ville an insulated rod in exact accordance with Franklin's description. At an experiment conducted by Dalibard during a storm on

May 10, 1752, electrical sparks were first obtained from this rod. The electrical nature of a storm was thus proved, somewhat earlier than this was done by Franklin, yet in accordance with his method.

The technical details of these experiments by Franklin as well as by others are very interesting, for they demonstrate his considerable experimental ingenuity.

As we study the history of the development of Franklin's work, we are surprised by the speed with which Franklin's views were accepted by science. Despite the opposition on the part of a number of such leading scientists as Abbé Nollet [5] and Wilson,[6] Franklin's ideas made their way in science within a very short period and solidly. Of course, a scientific truth will always find its way into life, but making this path a quick and a straighter one depends on people, not on the truth itself. In this respect Franklin's activity even to this day can serve as an example of how one must go about putting his scientific achievements into practice.

Franklin strove to make each and every one of his researches accessible at once to the widest possible range of people. In his home city of Philadelphia he organized some local citizens into a philosophical society, and before that society he demonstrated his researches and delivered lectures. Franklin visited foreign countries often, and there too he was on close terms with the scientific community. Franklin was in intensive correspondence on scientific subjects with a number of leading savants of France, Italy, and England, even when America and England were at war with each other. He learned, all by himself, the French, Italian, and Spanish languages. He also knew Latin.

His ability to fight for new ideas was revealed with a particular force when he began to put the lightning rod into active service. But we will speak of this later on. Right now let us return to the question of the further progress of Franklin's work in electricity.

Because of Franklin's ideas, scientists of many countries busied themselves with experiments that would explain the nature of electricity. In our country, in St. Petersburg, Lomonosov and Rikhman [7] built rods while studying atmospheric electricity, calling them "the thunder machine."

Unfortunately, Lomonosov's work, not only in the field of electricity, but particularly in chemistry where he was the first to discover the law of preservation of matter, although bearing a fundamental significance, could not nevertheless exert as great an influence on the forward pace of the world's science as it doubtless deserved.

It seems to me that the main reason for this lies in the social conditions amid which Lomonosov lived and did his creative work—conditions which gave him no opportunity to be in touch with savants of other countries and visit abroad. The isolation of Lomonosov's and Rikhman's work also, without doubt, hindered the influence of Russian science upon world science.

Rikhman's fate is particularly sad. In his works Rikhman correctly pointed out that any further development of Franklin's experiments should proceed in the direction of finding a quantitative description of electrification phenomena. It was while searching during a storm for a method of such a quantitative measurement of the charge in that electrified rod, or "the thunder machine," that Rikhman—wishing to make a quantitative count—bent over incautiously and approached the conductor too closely. He was instantly killed by the electrical discharge striking his head. This happened in 1753.

Following Franklin's work, the most important phase in the development of the science of electricity was the move toward the quantitative description of electric phenomena. This was done by Coulomb,[8] as late as 1785. We all know how, using his torsion balance, he discovered his fundamental law of interaction of electric charges. Coulomb found that the force of interaction depends on the square of the distance between the charges.

The theoretical works which followed, by Gauss,[9] Laplace,[10] and Poisson,[11] developed this basic law of nature into that harmonious theory of the electrostatic field which we use so widely in our days. But there is, in the history of the development of the study of the electric field, one comparatively little-known page which is related to Franklin's fundamental works and which it is of interest to recall.

Nearly one hundred years after Coulomb's work, in 1877, Maxwell published an article about Henry Cavendish's [12] unpublished works in electricity. In his capacity as the very first director of the Cavendish Laboratory at Cambridge, which was built thanks to the contributions of Cavendish's descendants, Maxwell was given access to the papers of Henry Cavendish. Among these papers Maxwell found Cavendish's manuscript, entirely ready for publication, which on the basis of Cavendish's experiments proved the very same law of the square of the distance between electrical charges discovered by Coulomb. The experimental proof as furnished by Cavendish was quite different from Coulomb's experiment; the method was simpler, and the facts of the proof were more precise than those given by Coulomb. There was no date on the Cavendish manuscript, but Maxwell placed the year as being under no circumstances later than 1775, that is, at least a decade earlier than Coulomb's discovery of that law.

In his work Cavendish used as his premise the possibility of proving theoretically that, in a hollow metallic conductor, the entire electric charge may distribute itself on the exposed surface only if these charges push away from one another according to the law of the square of the distance. But the spread of the charge on the conductor's exposed surface had already been proved by Franklin in his experiment with an electrically charged teakettle and a chain, about which I have spoken earlier. It was, however, necessary to find a way of making this proof more accurate.

Therefore Cavendish repeated this experiment in a more precise way. Instead of the kettle he took a hollow metallic sphere; in lieu of the chain he placed inside, concentrically, a second metallic sphere. Both spheres could be either isolated from each other or interlocked, depending on the need. Cavendish chose concentric spheres because this form of bodies

41

provided an opportunity to work quantitatively on the result obtained from the experiment. The experiment by Cavendish was to prove that the charge, relayed to the exterior sphere, spread only upon that sphere and did not extend itself to the interior sphere.

At Cambridge, Maxwell organized a replica of Cavendish's experiment, but, thanks to his improved measuring instrument, he proved that Coulomb's law of the second degree is correct with a precision of almost one-millionth part, while Coulomb's method of using a torsion balance could check this law with an exactitude of no more than one per cent.

Here the question arises as to why for one hundred years such outstanding scientists as Gauss, Poisson, Laplace, and other creators of the theory of the electrical field failed to notice that Franklin's simple experiment could already serve for a practical proof of the correctness of one of the most basic laws of the electrostatic field—the Coulomb law.

How could it happen that Cavendish's work remained totally unknown for one hundred years? In his article Maxwell also points out that in the very same manuscript by Cavendish, ready for publication, in addition to the Coulomb law there was formulated and roughly checked also what we now know as Ohm's law. And this was done seventy years before this law was discovered by Ohm [13] himself.

It is natural to ask how it could happen that such a great scientist as Cavendish, called by many "the Newton of modern chemistry," could and did neglect to publish this work on electricity, which, of course, he could not help but consider as basic.

History may never find an answer to this question. The likeliest solution to the puzzle is that Cavendish simply forgot to have the manuscript published.

This explanation may at first glance seem improbable, for (it would appear) his friends, other scientists, should have known about these papers and should have reminded him of them. But here a singular characteristic of Cavendish is revealed: he had no friends of any kind at all; he generally avoided people. He was a very wealthy man, a brother of the Duke of Devonshire, but his mode of life was exceptionally solitary. He lived for science only. In his palace chambers even his servants were forbidden to come within his sight. His food was served before he would enter his dining room. It was because of this isolation from humans that Cavendish's scientific work, the fruit of his greatest scientific discoveries, made in England, failed to influence the development of the world's science.

Much later, French scientists discovered these laws of nature independently. They communicated their knowledge to mankind, and now these basic laws of nature justly bear the names of Coulomb and Ohm.

Besides his purely scientific works, Franklin has an outstanding technological achievement to his name. Generally recognized as his, this is the invention of the lightning rod. There is also much that is instructive in the history of putting this invention into use. It is a long story, much researched by others. Here I will give you but a brief account of Franklin's invention and introduction of the lightning rod.

I have already mentioned that Franklin proved experimentally that lightning is nothing but an electric spark, arising between the clouds and the ground when they possess electric countercharges. After the essence of the thunderstorm's charge was thus proved, the question naturally arose as to how it would be possible rationally to combat the destruction and fires caused by lightning. It became clear that when lightning strikes a building, a ship, or any other elevated object, the damage comes from the mighty electrical current which, passing through a medium of poor conductivity, causes destruction and fires. Therefore, given an opportunity to pass through such a good-conductivity medium as metal, lightning striking a building will cause no damage. It became clear why buildings with roofs and rain pipes made of metal were less vulnerable to the action of storm clouds' discharges. For instance, Solo-

43

mon's temple in Jerusalem not once in a thousand years was subject to any storm-caused destruction, for it was covered with sheets of polished metal.

It was only natural that, following Franklin's researches, which had revealed the nature of thunderstorm discharges, a number of individuals at once began to have ideas about the possibility of antilightning defense by deflecting the electric discharge through metallic rods of good conductivity.

It is entirely possible that in 1754, in a small Czech town, that modest priest named Prokop Divish acted on his own when, on the basis of his understanding of the processes of electric discharges, and using a grounded chain as a conductor to deflect the current, he installed over the roof of his house a contraption closely resembling Franklin's lightning rod. The priest's gadget had a sad end, for the little town's denizens, moved by a superstitious fear, tore off and destroyed the installation.

Undoubtedly, Franklin with his sharp practical mind perceived well ahead of all the others the possibility of finding defense against lightning by deflecting the current. But it was much more difficult for him to evolve a most rational form of his lightning rod and to win his era's general recognition for this rod as an effective instrument of combating thunderstorm-wrought destruction. Franklin managed this task brilliantly, and his activity in this area can to this day serve as a model in our endeavors to implement new technical ideas in actual life.

Franklin not only would not take out a patent for his lightning rod but even offered an opportunity of using the rod free of charge to anyone who wished it. Besides, widely and successfully he propagandized the practical introduction of his invention. I will not tell in full the history of the lightning rod's introduction, but will dwell only on its more prominent moments.

It is quite possible that not a single invention has ever caused such a storm of all sorts of objections as did, two centuries ago, this small metallic rod, which in our time crowns almost every building as a standard ingredient of each and every edifice.

The objections against the lightning rod two hundred years ago were of all kinds, indeed. They stemmed from most divergent premises. There were such arguments as "In the hands of Providence, lightning is an instrument of punishment, and therefore it is sinful to oppose it." Another no less convincing objection was: "Thunderstorms occur when evil spirits and demons disobey the Almighty." Thus, it was said, the only right way to combat them was by the ringing of church bells to chase the evil spirits away. That is why for such a long time it was considered necessary to ring church bells during a thunderstorm. Yet, it was not at all safe to ring church bells during a storm, since church bells are most vulnerable to lightning. Even after the lightning rod's invention, such rods for a long time were not installed on churches, and church-bell ringing was continued during storms. In Germany, in the late eighteenth century, in thirty-three years one hundred twenty church-bell ringers were killed and four hundred church belfries were destroyed by lightning.

But Franklin's principal fight for his lightning rod was carried on by him not against these superstitious and religious objections, which came from the less cultured strata of the populace. His struggle was against the very top of his time's society, where he met scientific as well as political arguments against his lightning rod.

In Franklin's descriptions of the lightning rod's action, he pointed not only to the rod's obvious function of providing for the current a direct path along the metal rod into the ground, but also to the possibility that there might be yet another process.

Franklin considered that, should there be a thundercloud over a building, and were the lightning rod furnished with a sharp edge, a slow flow of the electric charge down that edge might occur. We now call this phenomenon "the silent discharge." This is what neutralizes and discharges the cloud's charge. Franklin argued that his lightning rod not only pro-

45

tected a building but could generally prevent thunderstorm discharges. But on their part, Franklin's scientific opponents felt that the flow of the charge from the sharp edge would not only fail to neutralize the cloud's charge but would even create more favorable conditions for the creation of lightning. The lightning rod was therefore rather harmful, they said, for it led to a creation of thunderstorm discharges which otherwise, without the rod, would not have generally happened.

The scientists who held this belief considered as an especially dangerous situation that in which a building was next to another structure possessing a lightning rod.

Public interest in such problems was quite acute, as witnessed by the well-known case of the lightning rod installed by Monsieur de Vissery on the roof of his house in Saint Omer, France. His neighbors, in fright and indignation, filed a court suit against him. The suit caused much sensation and lasted several years, 1780 to 1784. It is of interest that the lightning rod was in this case defended by a young lawyer named Maximilien Robespierre. This sensational suit in fact was the start of his renown. It is also curious to note that one of the plaintiffs' experts was Marat, who held that the lightning rod was a dangerous gadget. He spoke against its installation. After a long struggle and several appeals, de Vissery won the case.

Franklin's tactics in all this fight for his lightning rod are of interest.

It was his custom not to deliver public speeches about it. Instead, by conversations and by his enormous correspondence he incessantly influenced his era's leading savants and public men. With such propaganda he created for himself a mighty army from among the forward-thinking men of his time, and this army then carried on the fight to put into practice his brain child, the lightning rod.

In England, the campaign against the lightning rod assumed a sharply political character. The English scientist Wilson attempted to prove that it was possible to avoid the lightning rod's harmful effects by blunting its edge so as to prevent the flow of the charge. Since the period of this debate coincided with the epoch of America's liberation from colonial rule, and since Franklin then became an important political figure in young America as one of her most active fighters for her freedom, each and every inhabitant of England who would not blunt his lightning rod's edge was considered politically unreliable.

England's King George III demanded of the Royal Society, that country's academy of sciences, a cancellation of its decision in favor of a sharp edge atop Franklin's lightning rod. To this demand, Sir John Pringle, president of the Royal Society, the King's physician and Franklin's personal friend, gave the celebrated answer that, both by his duty and his inclinations, he to the best of his strength would always obey His Majesty's wishes, but he would not be able to change either the laws of nature or the action of its forces. For these words he was discharged as the King's physician and deprived of the presidency of the Royal Society.

In the course of this fight over the lightning rod, all kinds of slander, insinuation, and similar methods of attacks were used against Franklin personally as well as against his friends. Franklin preserved his great calm, paying no heed to personal attacks, and invariably saying that in the problems of science the truth will come out through experiment and experience only.

Indeed, precisely this—experiment and experience—resolved the debate, but this happened many decades later, when the teachings about thunderstorm discharges and the electrical field reached their modern forms. Now we know that this entire debate had no basis whatsoever, for it makes absolutely no difference whether the top point of an ordinary lightning rod is sharp or blunt. At a short distance from the ground the geometrical form of the lightning rod's edge cannot perceptibly influence the distribution of the electric field over the ground.

Yet, Dr. Schoenland, one of the leading experts on thunderstorm discharges, points out that the process of neutralization of the cloud's charge by way of a silent discharge can nevertheless be effected, but only when the sharp top of the lightning rod is situated so high above the ground that its height may be compared to the height of a cloud. This is valid for the lightning rods installed on the highest American skyscrapers, where indeed it is possible to observe, flowing from the sharp edge, a silent discharge which does not become a lightning. Schoenland adds that could Franklin have known this, it would have given him a justifiable feeling of satisfaction.

These days the lightning rod is an inevitable feature of all our construction. It is of course impossible to calculate the number of buildings, installations, and ships which this rod has safeguarded from fire and destruction. This is rightfully one of Franklin's contributions.

I will be brief on Franklin's activities in other areas of science, for, indeed, besides the already listed accomplishments, there are his achievements in other fields as well.

Franklin busied himself with geophysics; composed a map of the Gulf Stream; invented a musical instrument based on rubbing glass balls; built an economical stove, to this day used in America and France; introduced street lamps; created bifocals for old men's farsightedness—and much else, too. In addition, with his gregarious nature and lively mind Franklin was a frequent consultant and thus aided in the development of science. Of course, information about most of such consulting is lost to us, but some facts on this are nonetheless available.

Thus Louis XVI requested Franklin to join a committee which was considering the value of a healing method proposed by Dr. Mesmer on the basis of the so-called "animal magnetism." It is interesting to note that the rather well-known Dr. Guillotin, inventor of the guillotine, was a member of this committee. Franklin denied the existence of animal magnetism but remarked that this was a harmless method of treatment, since it amused wealthy people without causing them any damage, while the same could not always be said about other baseless methods of medical treatment.

Franklin very much approved the flights by the Montgolfier

brothers. We should also note that field of Franklin's activity, whereby he, as a prominent statesman of his time, could and did help the progress of the world's science.

Franklin felt that scientific achievements belonged to all mankind, that concern for the progress of world science should not be affected by the nation's political and military differences. Thus, during America's Revolutionary War, when Captain Cook, the famous explorer, was returning from his voyage, Franklin instructed all the American ships—regular and privateer—to respect Captain Cook no matter where they might encounter him. It is of interest to our era, too, that Franklin as a member of Congress prevailed upon his fellow legislators to exempt scientific equipment from the embargo placed on all cargoes of British origin.

As we study Franklin's life, we understand more and more clearly why there is this universal respect and admiration for this great man, this American gift to humanity.

In our epoch of the rapid growth of the natural sciences we realize that each nation has contributed a great pioneer of science. We gave Lomonosov to mankind; the English brought forth Newton; the Italians contributed Galileo; the Dutch produced Huyghens; the French, Descartes; the Germans, Leibniz; and the Americans, Franklin. The accomplishments of these great savants are the pride of all mankind.

And we the Soviet people are grateful to the American nation that gave and reared for humanity the great Franklin.

2

Lomonosov and the World of Science

[*This address on Mikhail V. Lomonosov (1711-1765) was delivered by Dr. Kapitsa at the session of the Division of Physics and Mathematics of the Soviet Academy of Sciences which took place at the Institute of Problems of Physics in Moscow on November 17, 1961. He later repeated some of the points of this address in his article, "Lomonosov i mirovaya nauka" (Lomonosov and world science), which appeared in* Sovetskaya Rossiya, Moscow, April 15, 1965.]

IT is indeed gratifying to speak of Lomonosov—to commune with one of the most original geniuses in the history of human culture. Yet it is also difficult to speak of Lomonosov, since, from our school days, we are all so well acquainted with his image and his work. It is hard to say anything new, because for two hundred years Lomonosov's life and labors have been studied and discussed so thoroughly. Among those who spoke and wrote about Lomonosov we find our most prominent writers, publicists, scientists, and statesmen: Radishchev,[1] Pushkin,[2] Belinsky,[3] Dobrolyubov,[4] Chernyshevsky,[5] Herzen (Gertsen),[6] Pisarev,[7] Aksakov,[8] Menshutkin,[9] Val'den (Walden),[10] Vavilov,[11] Fersman,[12] Komarov,[13] and many, many others. Although some facets of Lomonosov's work were at times criticized, all biographers and commentators with no exception whatever spoke of him with enormous devotion, recognizing his great influence on the development of our native culture—our language, literature, education, technology, and science. Lomonosov's high significance to the cause of progress was recognized before the Revolution; it is recognized now as well. Beginning already with the last century, the anniversary dates of his birth and death were marked without fail and most solemnly. In our time these are celebrated on a yet grander scale, with the participation of our entire nation.

The first monument to Lomonosov was erected in his native Arkhangelsk; its author was Martos,[14] our most talented sculptor of the time. Subscription of contributions to defray the cost of the monument was opened in 1825. Some short four years later the monument was unveiled.

In 1865, the centenary of Lomonosov's death, the Academy of Sciences established an annual one thousand ruble prize in his honor. Its award was alternated between the humanities and the natural sciences. In our time the Academy of Sciences has again established a Lomonosov prize and medal.

The only thing not done in the two hundred years elapsing since his death was the publication of Lomonosov's complete works. But this, too, has been accomplished in the last few years.

Few of our scientists or public figures have left so rich a heritage of biographic and historiographic material as is associated with Lomonosov. But as we become acquainted with this data, we cannot help but regret that not a single good portrait of Lomonosov has come down to our times. The portraits and engravings of him that are usually reproduced, were done posthumously. They are copies of one and the same original portrait painted by an unknown artist of scant talent. Only the bust by Shubin,[15] who had a personal acquaintance with Lomonosov, gives us an image that is alive, that relays his true spirit.

As we study sources on Lomonosov, we miss a depiction of him as a human being—none of our outstanding writers has done such a portrait in depth of him. Of course there have lived many scientists, some of them truly great, whose sphere of interest has been limited by the walls of their laboratories. Usually the human image of such scientists is of little interest. But when the activity of a great savant and an outstandingly original person, such as Lomonosov was, embraces the development of an entire nation's culture and, at that, within one of the most interesting and significant periods of its history, then his living image is of much interest to all mankind.

The greater the man the more contradictions there are in him—the more numerous contrasts can be found in the tasks and problems with which life confronts him. The range of these contradictions is indeed the measure of the genius in that man. The paradoxes in Lomonosov's own nature, as well as the conflicts amid which his life flowed, were extraordinarily great.

It is difficult to discover a greater contrast than we do in the fate of "the peasant from Arkhangelsk" living and working in the very heart of the courtier top of the officialdom and the nobility. Lomonosov was a public figure who did things for the sake of progress. He saw the necessity of education for people, the need for learning and science. He fought against superstitions and prejudices. And yet, to carry out his aims, he had to seek support among the grandees at the court. Despite his peasant origin, he understood the necessity to flatter, to praise those who held power, and he managed this problem in a way all his own. The brilliance of his personality brought him friendship and protection from most influential noblemen of the time, such as Shuvalov,[16] Vorontsov,[17] and Orlov.[18]

When Tsar Peter I "hacked open the window" to Europe, the Western wind carried into Russia not only culture and learning. Along with the real scientists, such as Euler [19] and Bernulli [20] were, the Western wind brought to us a large number of foreign scientists who were only average or even sheer adventurers, whose sole concern was their own material welfare, who strove to safeguard their privileged status in Russia which gave them their chance of quick enrichment. It was only natural that in the Academy of Sciences they tried to hinder the rise of a native Russian influence. It is well known that Lomonosov was compelled, with the support of the authority of some foreign scientists, to fight against the undue domination of foreigners. His acute mind enabled Lomonosov to appraise clearly the complexity of the circumstances amid which his work had to proceed. This complexity demanded of him much self-control and tact, and yet such qualities were counter to the inherent lack of restraint in his temperament, his passionate nature. Here rose those sharp clashes which we so well know in Lomonosov's biography. But the sum total of it was that Lomonosov's genius succeeded in triumphing in this complicated contest. Still, a really good picture of this complex struggle has not as yet been presented to us by any writer.

Lomonosov realized the great importance of the development of science in Russia and the need to raise the level of higher learning. He labored mightily in the establishment of the University of Moscow. He could not allot as much time to his researches as he wished to, and he drew young people into scientific work. Yet, apparently, he was not a born teacher. His excessive individualism prevented him from becoming a self-disciplined instructor of the young. The result was that, having expended so much effort to disseminate knowledge in Russia, he nevertheless left no disciples. Menshutkin, the best authority on Lomonosov's scientific activity, writes that "he created no school, and after his death his only pupil to devote himself to science was S. Ya. Rumovsky," later a professor of astronomy at the Academy of Sciences.

One could go on listing such paradoxes in Lomonosov's life, but the task still awaiting a major writer on this subject is that of re-creating Lomonosov's image so that it would be truly alive, an image containing all these contradictions.

At this point I would like to dwell on one of the contradictions in Lomonosov's life which, although well known, has not as yet found a proper explanation. I think that this paradox is important for us today, too.

In his lifetime Lomonosov repeatedly said that his activity as a poet and a writer, as a reformer of the Russian language, also as a historian, a civic leader, a geologist, and an administrator satisfied him but little, that he saw his basic calling in scientific work, in physics and chemistry. Indeed it would seem that his scientific toil in chemistry and physics should have been in his main activity, insofar as from 1741 on, that is, from the very beginning of his presence in the Academy of Sciences, he occupied the post of adjunct in physics and four years later was appointed professor of chemistry. It is natural to suppose that under these circumstances the genius of Lomonosov should have left the greatest possible trace in the world's science no less than in the science of his native country. But we know that this did not happen. The absence of such an impact has time and again puzzled many of those who have studied the history of science. Academician P. I. Val'den, in his speech at Lomonosov's jubilee celebration at the Academy of Sciences in 1911, examined this problem in detail. He pointed to "the tragic fate of Lomonosov's scientific work that left no visible traces in chemistry and physics." The speaker cited sufficient data which confirmed the fact that foreign historians did not know Lomonosov's scientific achievements.

There is no mention of Lomonosov's name whatever in the history of physics written by Heller and Rosenberger. The French historian of chemistry, Hoefer (1860), devoted to Lomonosov but a few lines, and rather curious ones, at that. Let me cite them verbatim: "Among the Russian chemists who became known as chemists, let us mention Michael Lomonosov, who should not be confused with the poet of the same name."

But if men of the West hardly knew Lomonosov's work as a physicist and a chemist, in Russia this work of his has remained either unknown or forgotten until very recently. Up to the dawn of the present century, in all the voluminous writings on the subject of Lomonosov there were just two essays on

Lomonosov the physicist, both published in the jubilee year of 1865. One of these two, by N. A. Lyubimov, is an inept summary of several of Lomonosov's researches in physics. The second, by N. P. Beketov, runs to but five brief pages. Nothing is said about Lomonosov's accomplishments as a physicist and a chemist in both large Russian encyclopedias, the one by Brokhaus as well as that by Granat, or in the Encyclopedia Britannica, or in the French Larousse. Not a single mention of Lomonosov could be found even in our fundamental course of physics by O. D. Khvol'son, the book which otherwise so thoroughly cited all the available literature in the field. Khvol'son's course repaired this omission only after Menshutkin's work on Lomonosov had begun to appear.

On the other hand, Alexander Pushkin in his notes entitled "A Journey from Moscow to St. Petersburg" (1834), while discussing Lomonosov's work, wrote: "Lomonosov himself did not value his poetry. He was much more concerned about his experiments in chemistry than about the odes which he was obliged to write in commemoration of the saint's day of his sovereign." Pushkin spoke of Lomonosov as a great leader of science. History remembers Pushkin's remarkable words about Lomonosov: "He was, so to say, our first university."

Pushkin saw the genius of Lomonosov as a scientist. We greatly appreciate Pushkin's opinion. He was one of the best educated men, who profoundly understood the Russian reality. Besides, Pushkin lived when he could yet meet people who had seen and heard Lomonosov in their lifetime. Thus Lomonosov was recognized as a great savant by his own contemporaries. But it is worth noting that no one of those around him could say what it was actually that Lomonosov had achieved in science, precisely why he should be considered a great scientist.

This state of affairs continued until the opening of our century, when Boris N. Menshutkin, a professor of physical chemistry, began—a scientist himself—to study Lomonosov's scientific contributions to chemistry and physics. Menshutkin translated Lomonosov's works from their Latin and German originals. He studied critically not only the basic works, but also Lomonosov's correspondence and personal notes. Starting with 1904, Menshutkin published this material systematically.[21] Later this labor was continued by S. I. Vavilov, T. P. Kravets, and other scholars. And this was how, only two hundred years later, we learned on what and how Lomonosov had worked.

Now, knowing as we do the path along which science has developed since Lomonosov, we can unerringly evaluate his scientific work in chemistry and physics. Thus it has become clear only now that, for its time, Lomonosov's scientific endeavor was in the very forefront and should have doubtless left a deep imprint on the progress of the world's science. Pushkin's intuitive appraisal of Lomonosov as a great scientist, voiced more than one hundred years ago, leaves us at a loss as to the reasons for the neglect of all this scientific activity of Lomonosov's, of its failure to exert its influence, not only in foreign countries, but also in our own country.

We must speak of this sadly, for, as a result of this gap, both our science and the world's science have suffered a considerable loss. Of course, such an isolation of Lomonosov from the world's science could not happen accidentally. It had its historic causes. I think that we have had quite a few of such cases where discoveries and achievements of Russian savants did not make a deserved impact on the progress of the world's science. Therefore the contradictions between Lomonosov's greatest accomplishments in science on the one hand, and the absence of their proper influence upon the development of the world's science on the other, are of interest these modern days, too. Let me dwell on this problem in more detail.

In order to analyze the connection between Lomonosov's work as a scientist and the science of his time, it is necessary to sketch, even if in its general features, the picture of the conditions under which the natural sciences progressed in the first half of the eighteenth century. Let us remember that, in the history of man's culture, only the sixteenth century may be considered as the beginning of the intensive growth of the natural sciences. It is true that up to that time mankind had also known such great savants as Pythagoras, Archimedes, and Avicenna, but they were lone geniuses. Science at that time developed slowly. Only from the sixteenth century on did science begin to develop in accelerating tempos, as a result of the fact that scientific work had emerged as men's collective creation on a scale that became international. We well know the first enormous successes of this collective creation by scientists: this was the rapid growth of astronomy and mechanics. Its participants were Copernicus the Pole, Tycho Brahe the Dane, Kepler the German, Galileo the Italian, Newton the Englishman, Descartes the Frenchman, Huyghens the Dutchman, and many, many other less-known scientists.

To this day, too, collective work by scientists on a worldwide scale remains the basic factor guaranteeing a rapid growth of science. This growth became possible not only thanks to the rise of the material well-being of mankind and the development of means of communication among nations, but, chiefly, because of the invention of printing in the fifteenth century. All scholars well understand that, to this day, neither the dissemination nor the preservation of scientific experience and scientific achievements is possible without books. Without this dissemination and this preservation, science of course cannot develop to its full value.

In the same historic period, science broke off from theology, and this was necessary if science was to develop on a sound materialistic basis. From that time on, leading statesmen began to comprehend the importance of the progress of the natural sciences for the growth of human culture. Already in the beginning of the seventeenth century, Francis Bacon clearly formulated the enormous significance of studying nature through experiments, of the inductive method in generalizing these experiments, which method leads to the understanding of laws of nature. A first-rate statesman, who had reached the post of lord chancellor, Bacon was convicted in 1621 on charges of taking bribes. He spent the end of his life in semi-exile, where he wrote those philosophical works which made his name immortal. Thus did disgrace during his lifetime become glory after his death. In these writings, particularly in his unfinished *New Atlantis,* he resurrected in a new way the history of Plato's Atlantis. This island lives because of scientists. Scientists rule it. In his description of the island it is possible to find scientific institutes and other features of an organized scientific life that remind us of our [Soviet] state organization of science.

The importance of science is a mighty force guiding the growth of a country's culture along the right path is shown by Bacon in this beautiful example wherein science is contrasted with empiricism: "A lame cripple, walking along the right road, can overtake a race horse if the horse runs along a wrong way. Moreover, the faster the race horse runs along this wrong road, the farther will the cripple be ahead."

It was also Bacon who declared that physics is "the mother of all sciences," the first to show the way of the development of man's culture. I am citing this in such detail because in those times Bacon's works were widely read and his *New Atlantis* went through many editions. His views were current among the ruling strata of the advanced nations, and at this particular time the development of science was considered a state's concern. It was also at this time that scientific activity was so widespread that the need of coordinating it became apparent. Therefore already in the seventeenth century, academies of sciences or similar scientific societies began to be formed in many countries. Scientific journals and memoirs were then being printed for the first time.

Tsar Peter I, while visiting Western Europe, at once comprehended the importance of science for the development of any country. He could not fail to understand that Russia also needed science to become a front-rank, civilized land. The celebrated conversations on this subject took place at this point between Peter and Leibniz; the idea of creating an academy of sciences in Russia emerged. Our Academy was established in 1725, after Peter's death, when his widow, Catherine I, reigned. It is well known that the Academy was formed with foreigners as its members, so that they would help mold Russian scientists. Lomonosov was lucky: he came to St. Petersburg in time to become one of the first Russian scientists in the Academy of Sciences. But, of course, the Academy was even luckier—to have Lomonosov as its first Russian scientist. He had obtained his higher scientific education in Germany, where for five years he had studied chiefly under Professor Christian Wolff.[22] In 1741 Lomonosov returned to St. Petersburg, where he had to begin his scientific work under most unfavorable circumstances.

By that time the Academy of Sciences had existed already nearly twenty years. This was during the reign of Empress Anna and the rule by Biron,[23] her favorite. Peter's idea of developing Russia's own science was relegated to a secondary place.

When the Academy of Sciences was first established, there were only two truly first-rate scientists among all the invited foreigners, and both were to become famous. These were Leonhard Euler and Daniel Bernulli. But the attention with which they had initially been surrounded steadily diminished. In 1741, when Lomonosov returned from Germany to St. Petersburg, both of them—first Bernulli, and then Euler—quit the Academy. It is of interest to note that Euler left St. Petersburg three days before Lomonosov's return from Germany. Euler returned to St. Petersburg years later, when Catherine II was the ruler, and when scientists once more began to be deferred to. Thus, although Lomonosov and Euler exchanged much correspondence, they never met, if we do not count the possible attendance at Euler's lectures by Lomonosov before his departure for Germany.

And so, at the Academy of Sciences, in his work in physics and chemistry, Lomonosov was practically alone. To know the latest in science he had to consult literature, which at that time was quite scarce. He had no personal contact with the era's prominent scientists, since Lomonosov ceased traveling to foreign lands after his student days, and foreign scholars did not come to visit him in St. Petersburg, inasmuch as the Academy of Sciences of the time was not worth-while.

59

And yet, this isolation from the world of science notwithstanding, Lomonosov managed to concentrate his work on the most crucial problems of chemistry and physics of that period. As a scientist, he combined in himself both the thinker and the experimenter. Of interest to us are his statements on the connection between theory and experiment. His words are completely valid for our times, too. He said: "Some theoreticians, omitting to do any preliminary experimentation whatever, make evil use of their leisure by inventing empty and false theories and by overloading our literature with these...."

Experiment was placed by Lomonosov at the head of his study of nature. This was his characteristic feature as a scientist. That was why he exerted so much effort to create a laboratory; that was why he worked there so assiduously. But his contemporaries little valued Lomonosov as a savant. He was appreciated, first of all, as a poet. For one of his laudatory odes he received from the Tsarina the sum of two thousand rubles, which was more than his three years' salary at the Academy of Sciences (this was 660 rubles per annum).

Too, Lomonosov was respected as a historian, also as the creator of the literary Russian language—for his grammar, for his translations. And he was valued for his statesmanlike concern about the progress of education and technology in Russia.

Officialdom and courtiers did not comprehend the significance of his scientific work in the laboratory. To justify his laboratory hours, Lomonosov wrote to Count Shuvalov in 1753: "I presume that I may be allowed a few hours daily so as to use them for experiments in physics and chemistry instead of playing billiards...." Thus was Lomonosov compelled to excuse his scientific work on the grounds that, after all, he was giving up his leisure time and billiard game for it. But of course another justification of spending state money on the laboratory was in the latter's practical results, as for instance the mosaic glass that came out of it, also the solution of various technical problems.

We stand in awe before the wealth of Lomonosov's achievements in the area of experimental, basic science—his great accomplishments despite those unfavorable conditions amid which he worked. First of all, in his work he very widely embraced different fields of physics. He studied the liquid, solid, and gasiform states of bodies. He worked out thermometry carefully; he calibrated his mercuric thermometers exactly. Using these, he, for instance, ascertained the coefficient of the expansion of gases, when heated, with a precision remarkable for his time. As we compare his results with such data of our time, we find that his error was one of less than three per cent, and that his figures were ten times more correct than the levels recognized as true in his era. This shows an exceptionally high technique for Lomonosov as an experimenter. To list Lomonosov's other ahcievements in the field of experimental physics and chemistry, which reached the same superior level, would take too much time; nor is this our task. Those who are interested in this question can read Boris N. Menshutkin's excellent monograph, published in 1947, on Lomonosov's work in physics and chemistry.

There is no doubt that these works of Lomonosov's by themselves should have placed him among that era's most important experimenters. Curiously enough, Lomonosov's experiments in electricity are better known, not because of their scientific results, but because they caused the death of Rikhman, who was killed during such experiments. The experiments of Franklin, his contemporary, were known to him, and he repeated them, but Lomonosov's main interest was in the questions dealing with atmospheric electricity. He connected the origin of this electricity with the rising and descending streams of air which always accompany storm clouds. This view is to this day held to be correct, but the mechanism of the emergence of the cloud's charge is so difficult to study that to this time it has not been completely ascertained.

He also did a number of optical experiments. These boiled down to the construction of more perfect optical instruments, of a telescope-reflector, for example, with the aid of which Lomonosov observed in 1761 that rare phenomenon—the passing of the sun's disc by Venus. These observations also proved to be an important contribution to science. He noticed the deformation and the blurredness of the edges of the disc of Venus and by this was the first to show that Venus must possess an atmosphere. It is worth noting that modern manuals of astronomy say that the same proof was obtained only in 1882, that is 121 years later, when Venus again passed through the sun's disc.

The most significant of Lomonosov's accomplishments was his experimental proof of the "Law of Preservation of Matter." By now Lomonosov's discovery of this law has been well studied, and Lomonosov's priority in this discovery is established completely and beyond any doubt. It was in 1756 that he carried out his classic experiment proving that, as a sealed container is heated, its leaden plates undergo an oxidation, but the container's total weight does not change. This experiment by Lomonosov is analogous to the famous experiment by Lavoisier, but Lavoisier's experiment came seventeen years later. I will not repeat this entire history in its detail, for most people know it all. Doubtless, this discovery of one of nature's most fundamental laws should place Lomonosov's name in the history of science side by side with the world's greatest scientists.

But all these works of Lomonosov's were largely unknown not only outside Russia. Even in Russia, up to the researches by Menshutkin, most of these works were not known either. It is clear that, under such circumstances, Lomonosov's works in physics and chemistry could not exert their deserved influence on the development of our science as well as the world's science.

How did it all happen?

It may seem that the primary reason for this scant foreign knowledge of Lomonosov's work could lie in the fact that he himself might have attached little importance to the priority of his discoveries, that he was possibly remiss in publicizing his work sufficiently. But priority in scientific work was valued in those days not less than it is now. It is enough to recall the argument between Newton and Leibniz over the priority of the invention of differential calculus, the argument which in time took the form of a serious diplomatic incident, during which episode Leibniz' career suffered gravely.

Documents coming down to our times contain proof that Lomonosov indeed valued priorities, and therefore did publish his works, some in Latin, some in German. He had excellent command of both languages. As witness of Lomonosov's concern that his scientific work should be known abroad let us cite this fact:

In 1753, when Rikhman was killed by lightning, the general meeting of the Academy of Sciences was postponed, but Lomonosov requested that he be allowed to deliver his speech about electricity "while it has not lost its novelty." Therefore Count Razumovsky,[24] president of the Academy of Sciences, ordered that on the day of the celebration of the coronation [25] a solemn assembly be held, "so that Mr. Lomonosov with his new works would not be late among Europe's learned men, and so that his labors in the electric experiments so far carried out would not be lost." Following this, the text of Lomonosov's speech was sent to many foreign scholars.

It is also known that Lomonosov wrote of his work to Euler and to a number of other scientists. We should recall that, at that time, personal correspondence among savants was regarded as one of the most effective methods of spreading scientific information; this method was used by all widely. Thus there is no ground whatever to believe that either here or abroad scientists could not know about Lomonosov's work. They indeed knew his work, but they did not pay enough attention to it.

Some biographers of Lomonosov have suggested that the lack of attention for Lomonosov's work stemmed from the fact that his ideas were too far ahead of their time. I think that this guess is also groundless. It is true that Lomonosov's lively and bold mind grasped almost all the fields of natural science which were within the interests of his era's "natural philosophy." For breadth of scope it is difficult to name another scholar contemporary to Lomonosov and equal to him in his many-faceted interests and knowledge. Lomonosov's theoretical concepts in those fields of science where he directly participated with his experimental work, such as the theory of heat, the state of matter, chemistry, are astonishing in the channels they follow—the very same channels along which they have developed in those fields after Lomonosov and to this day.

The modern reader is astounded by the fact that Lomonosov had a perfectly clear idea of the kinetic nature of heat. Lomonosov graphically connected the warming up of a body with the increase in the forward motion and the gyration of atoms and molecules, which were given by him other names, of course. Although these views of Lomonosov were advanced, he was not alone in professing them. They were, for instance, shared also by Bernulli. Lomonosov developed them with an extraordinary consistency and logic. He came face to face, for example, with the concept of the absolute zero. In paragraph twenty-six of his reflections "On Heat and Cold" he spoke "of the highest possible degree of cold, caused by an absolute quietude of particles, by a complete cessation of their movement."

To illustrate Lomonosov's conviction that he was right in his concept of the physical essence of heat, let us cite the following curious fact: In 1761 Lomonosov wrote a paper "On Multiplication and Preservation of the Russian People." In this paper he considered the various reasons responsible for a high mortality in Russia, and he proposed a number of measures to combat it. Thus, in his paragraph seven, he wrote that it was necessary to baptize babies in warm water always: "The priests follow the Missal's instructions that the water should be natural, with no admixtures, and they mistake warmth for an admixed matter, without stopping to think that in the summer they themselves baptize babies in warm water, even though the warmth in their opinion is an admixture, and so they contradict themselves. Nor do they in the shortness of their minds know that even the coldest water still contains a lot of warmth. However, there is no point to explain physics to those ignorant priests."

64

It is of interest to note that this paper was never published while the tsars were on their throne, for the ideas expressed therein were too revolutionary.

Lomonosov's ideas which guided his work in chemistry were also perfectly correct and advanced. He always took the atomistic concept as his premise; he came close to the idea of the molecular structure of chemical compounds. In his scientific researches in chemistry he considered it necessary to apply the qualitative method. He worked out precise methods of weighing. He considered it important to use the cleanest possible reagents. It was this qualitative approach to the study of chemical reactions that brought him to the need for an experimental proof of the law of preservation of matter. All this allows us to say that Lomonosov was the founder of the introduction of physical methods of research in the field of chemistry, as chemistry was understood in the eighteenth century.

In the field of wave optics Lomonosov together with Euler rightly supported the wave theory of light proposed by Huyghens, which, however, was not recognized because of the high authority of Newton, who stubbornly insisted on his mistaken corpuscular theory of light. But in his further development of the theory of light, Lomonosov took an erroneous path. The same happened to Euler.

Of much interest is Lomonosov's greatest mistake in one of the most fundamental problems of physics.

As is well known, Galileo discovered one of nature's most remarkable laws. He established that the mass of a body, regardless of its essence, is proportionate to the force of gravity, or, at a given point of space, simply to its weight. Newton demonstrated that this law is followed with a great precision. Newton's experiment was very simple, exact, and convincing. In his college room, in the doorway, he suspended two pendulums of the same length but made of different materials. He showed that the pendulums always swung strictly isochronously regardless of the material. This could happen only when the mass of a body was precisely proportionate to its weight. Lomonosov held that this was incorrect. He began to express himself on this subject in 1748 and continued to do so until 1757. All these statements by him date to a time considerably later than the period of Newton's pendulum experiments. Surprisingly, Lomonosov fought against this law for a long time after Newton's experiments. Thus in 1755 Lomonosov proposed to name as the problem theme, with a prize by the Academy of Sciences as a reward, an experimental investigation of "the hypothesis that the matter of bodies is proportionate to weight." Such a formulation, contradicting great Newton's views, met with objections in the Academy, and Euler was asked to be the judge. Euler, who usually sided with Lomonosov, in this case did not support him. He expressed himself against this formulation of the problem. It is necessary to note that Lomonosov's sole disciple, S. Ya. Rumovsky, also did not share Lomonosov's views on this, as witness his letters to Euler of 1757. Rumovsky, who later became a member of the Academy, had studied mathematics with Euler in Berlin for two years, and of course knew Newton's mechanics well. It is possible that at this point Rumovsky succeeded in convincing Lomonosov that he was in error, for in the post-1757 documents I find no indication that Lomonosov ever again raised this question.

Nothing is so instructive as an error by a genius. It seems to me that this particular mistake was not an accident, but that it had a deeper cause.

I believe that the reason for Lomonosov's error is connected with one philosophical concept, to which he mistakenly attached a universal significance. This concept was that motion in nature is always preserved—it never either emerges or vanishes, but is only relayed from one body to another, and at that through a direct touch solely. We know that this concept is correct in the case of balls resiliently striking one another. Now we also well know that, considering atoms' and molecules' collision as a clash between resilient spheres, it is possible to construct a complete, correct picture of the kinetic nature of heat. It is therefore understandable why Lomonosov, having on the one hand accepted the atomistic structure of matter, on the other subordinated the interaction between atoms to the laws of collision of resilient bodies and was thus the first to build correctly an almost complete picture of thermal phenomena on the basis of the kinetic concept. As I have already mentioned, he not only approached a definition of the absolute zero but also came face to face with the formulation of the law of preservation of energy, not generally of course but only where kinetic energy becomes thermal.

Lomonosov's error was that he gave his concept a universal character and began to feel that there exists in nature just one way of interaction between bodies, and this via touch. The possibility of action over distance via gravity or electrical interaction was denied by Lomonosov. Developing such concepts, he considered that, when a body assumed speed under the influence of weight, it was necessary for the medium surrounding the body to lose speed. The medium, capable of creating motion, was of course hypothetical, and Lomonosov postulated its existence in nature. In an analogous way he endeavored to depict also an electrical interaction between bodies. It is not difficult to understand that on the basis of such concepts not only did Lomonosov fail to draw a clear picture of phenomena connected with interaction of bodies over a distance, but he was also led by this to deny the existence of the universal connection between the weight and the mass of bodies.

It is difficult to understand how, in developing such views, Lomonosov could disregard Newton's pendulum experiments. It is possible that he either did not know or did not understand them. Nowhere in Lomonosov's writings could I find any mention of these experiments. As we examine Wolff's course of physics, which Lomonosov had studied and which later he translated into Russian, we are struck by the fact that the book does not pay enough attention to Newton's work in mechanics. There is no mention of Newton's pendulum experiment. It is of interest to observe that the only question of mechanics to which Wolff pays heed is precisely the collision of balls. I compared Christian Wolff's writings with those of other physicists of the period: I am left with the impression of Wolff as a scientist with limited thinking in the field of physics. It is known that his fame derived from his works on abstract philosophic themes. Apparently, Wolff failed to imbue Lomonosov with elements of a concrete mathematical thinking, without which it is difficult to absorb Newton's mechanics. As I have already pointed out, Lomonosov most likely had no opportunity to meet with such scientists as Bernulli and Euler, who not only knew Newton's mechanics well, but themselves became famous by developing it as a solid medium. We can confidently say that, had Lomonosov met them, he would not have committed his error.

The saddest thing in Lomonosov's life was that he could devote only a small share of his energy and time to his experimental work. However, given his great erudition and extraordinary imagination, perhaps no amount of time would have been sufficient to subject all of the hypotheses expressed by him to experimental checking. This was why it happened that, in the fields where Lomonosov worked experimentally, his theoretical and philosophical concepts were on the right road. But where he was divorced from things practical, and where he attempted to learn the truth through deduction, he often deviated from the right path. Had he been placed in such circumstances where he could do far more of his experimental work, had he for instance possessed many pupils, surely there would have been fewer of those erroneous hypotheses of his. What with his exceptional imagination, Lomonosov could have been the leader of a large scientific school. But, of proper conditions to create such a school in Russia at that time, there was not one.

And so, the explanation that Lomonosov was not recognized as a scientist because he was too far ahead of his time is groundless.

This is the time to recall that, generally speaking, in the history of Russian science, isolation of Russian scientists from the world's science has occurred often. I think that we should look for a general reason, a deeper one than the ones already discussed. But before we dwell on it, we may well remind ourselves briefly of another unrecognized Russian discovery, strongly resembling Lomonosov's case.

Very early in the nineteenth century, in Russia, a most remarkable discovery in physics was made, which also failed to make its proper impact on the world's science. This happened in 1802, when Vasily V. Petrov discovered the phenomenon of the electrical arc discharge in gas, which he named "voltaic arc." Now we all well know the entire tremendous role which the arc discharge subsequently played in science as well as in technology. But in our times it is hard indeed to appreciate properly all the difficulties of the first discovery of this fundamental phenomenon by Petrov. He did this eleven years after the discovery of galvanic current and only three years after the creation of the galvanic column by Volta. Of course, little was discovered about galvanic current in those intervening three years. Not only did Petrov himself have to make the batteries, consisting of 4,200 copper and zinc discs piled up in a column more than three meters long, but, also himself, he had to produce wire, which he insulated with sealing wax.

Petrov observed the arc discharge not only at a normal pressure, but also at a lowered one, as he passed the current in the bell of a vacuum pump. We may consider his uncovering of a discharge of such a type as his discovery of plasma. Although Petrov's work was at the time published in a separate brochure and sent to many scientific establishments, nevertheless the discovery of the arc discharge is usually credited to Davy,[26] who, however, achieved this only in 1810. Petrov also authored a number of interesting chemical researches in luminescence. Apparently he was the first one to accomplish decomposition of water by electrolysis, but all these activities also failed to make their proper impact on the world's science.

Petrov's life was most instructive. The son of a parish priest, he began his career as a modest provincial school teacher in Barnaul [Western Siberia] and in time reached the high post of professor of physics at the Medico-Surgical Academy in St. Petersburg. As Lomonosov, so also Petrov was a lone scientist, and he also left no school of disciples after him. His work and he himself remained unnoticed in the history of science, not only abroad, but also in our own country. No portrait of Petrov has been preserved, and his place of burial became known only recently. I have no doubt whatever that Vasily V. Petrov should occupy one of the foremost places not only in our science but also in the world's science as an outstanding physicist-experimenter.

We often hear that the lack of respect for the achievements of Russian scientists is explained by the fact that the Slavs' culture was usually regarded in the West as of a secondary role, not worth a place in the history of the world's culture. Such a view of the Slavs in general, and of Russians in particular, was quite common in the eighteenth and nineteenth centuries. But I think this is not a real answer to the question we pose here, since the history of science shows that true appraisal of great scientists' achievements was always made beyond national frontiers. After all, take Copernicus: he was recognized, although he was a Slav. Let us recall also that Euler repeatedly spoke in high praise of Lomonosov's work. Besides, this does not explain why we ourselves have so underestimated the scientific activity of Lomonosov, of Petrov, and of a number of other Russian savants.

It seems to me that an explanation should be sought in the conditions under which science develops in a given country. It is not enough for a scientist to make a scientific discovery for it to exert its influence upon the progress of the world's culture. It is imperative that, in the country in question, there should exist certain conditions, that there should be present a necessary connection with the scientific community abroad. In the absence of such conditions even such remarkable scientific works as those by Lomonosov and Petrov will not have their influence on the development of the world's culture.

I wish to dwell on such conditions as were necessary in Lomonosov's time—just as they are important in our days, too.

As I have already said, from the seventeenth century on, thanks to the collaboration of scientists on an international scale, the natural sciences began to expand faster than had been the case earlier. This could and did happen only because all these sciences are the same, if they develop on an experimental basis. Precisely this essence of oneness of materialistic science was responsible for its development through the broad international friendship of scientists. The pattern of this international collaboration by scientists is well known. In our days it is the same as it was in Lomonosov's time. Various countries have their own groups of scientific workers, which cluster at the universities, academies, or other scientific institutions. Insofar as each scientific field or problem can develop only in one direction, the forward movement is slow, and much energy is expended in research, so that the true road will not be lost. Collaboration in scientific work is successful exactly when these labor-consuming researches are distributed among the collectives of scientists working on a given problem. When a scientist works outside a collective, his results usually remain unnoticed.

Life inevitably proves that such a collective activity of scientists inside a country as well as on an international scale is possible only when there is a person-to-person contact. A scientist, in order to gain recognition for his scientific work, must not only publish this work but must also convince people of his toil's justice, must prove its significance. All this can be done successfully only when there is this person-to-person contact. As in Lomonosov's era, so in our own time, for a scientist's work to influence collective work, such a person-to-person contact is necessary, as is a lively exchange of opinion, and the opportunity for a discussion. All of this cannot be replaced by either printed word or correspondence. It is not so easy to explain why this is so. I think that most of us know from our own experience how this personal contact is needed among humans as they coordinate their creative activity. Only when you see a man and his laboratory, as you hear the intonation of his voice and behold the expression of his face, do you feel trust in his work and wish to work with him. For the very same reason no textbook can replace a teacher.

Nowadays the necessity of personal contacts among scientists is taken for granted by both our and foreign scientists. These contacts grow constantly and now take place on a wide scale through congresses and meetings.

Already in Lomonosov's time personal meetings between scientists were frequent. This was how it happened. A leading center of scientific work emerged in a given field of knowledge in this country or that. Such a center naturally attracted other scientists, men who frequently worked all by themselves. In the eighteenth century science was strongest in England. This was due to that country's wealth, which was exceptional for that time, and which produced philanthropists who supported science, so that it could and did develop more broadly. Like Lomonosov in Russia, Franklin in America was a lone scientist—and he journeyed to England. He succeeded in winning recognition for his remarkable work in electricity when he reported it to the Royal Society in London. It was also after a trip to London that Anton van Leeuwenhoek [27] achieved complete recognition for his work on the microscope, which had at first been met with distrust.

The tragedy of the isolation from the world's science suffered by Lomonosov, Petrov, and other solitary scientists of Russia stemmed solely from the fact that they could not join the collective work of foreign scientists, since they had no opportunity to travel to foreign lands. This, then, is the answer to the question posed by us—why the lack of their work's influence upon the world's science.

We have yet to dwell on the question of why Lomonosov's scientific work did not for a long time receive its recognition in Russia itself. It is perfectly clear that for a scientist to achieve recognition it is necessary for the society surrounding him to be at a level high enough to understand and appreciate the essence of his work. Neither the administrative, official personnel nor the courtiers around Lomonosov could of course comprehend the significance of his scientific work. Therefore recognition of his work in physics and chemistry became possible only when our country had gained a scientific community all her own.

Lomonosov and the World of Science

It is necessary to ponder this lesson of history in order to appreciate the enormous role played by society in the organization of science. Today this is very important for us, for we have before us the task of creating a most advanced science.

It is well known that for any creative work to develop successfully its practitioner must be in close contact with the society of his time and country. A writer, an actor, a musician, an artist creates at the fullness of his genius and further enhances his talent in no other way except through his connection with his society. A scientist's creativity also cannot develop successfully outside his collective milieu. Moreover, just as the level of a nation's art is shaped by the tastes and culture of the nation's society, so is the level of science set by the degree of development of the social conscience and activity of that nation's scientific community. Lomonosov's tragedy was deepened by the fact, which I have already mentioned, that in his time our country lacked such social-mindedness on the part of the scientists. The absence of a sound, critical collective made it difficult for Lomonosov to see precisely where in his search he was proceeding correctly and just where he had strayed.

This is why Lomonosov could not put to work the full strength of his genius. He painfully reacted to the absence of understanding and recognition for his work in his own country as well as abroad. Never did he derive that complete happiness from his creativity to which the might of his genius fully entitled him.

It is not hard to see that, for a science to progress to a leading place, the existence of a social responsibility and activity on the scientists' part is essential. Were we to fail in the creation of such a high-level responsibility and activity, we would not create an advanced science in our country, no matter how many Lomonosovs might be born here in Russia. To establish a sound, advanced, social-minded, and active scientific community is an important task. As yet not enough attention has been paid to this problem. This task is more difficult than the education of talented youths tapped for scientific work, more difficult, too, than the construction of large institutes. The creation of a sound social-mindedness and activity includes the enlightenment of wide strata of people connected with scientific work. They have to be trained to be interested in science broadly, to respect and love their particular science, to be able to appraise objectively the accomplishments of any science, and to support everything in science that is indeed important and best. After all, it is only such a social-mindedness and activity on the scientists' part that can correctly evaluate a scientific achievement, that can help a scientist proceed along a right road.

Only such a progressive social-mindedness of the scientists can appreciate the knowledge-producing strength of a scientific achievement, regardless of its immediate practical significance.

All the natural sciences can develop in the right direction if only they seek support in such a healthy civic awareness and activity of the scientists. As I have already noted, we discovered and recognized Lomonosov at the beginning of the twentieth century not accidentally but solely because by that time this nation had witnessed the beginning growth of our own sound social-mindedness on the part of our scientists. And this phenomenon grew in our field of physics when material conditions for scientific research improved, making it possible for that period's great scientists—Lebedev,[28] Rozhdestvensky,[29] Lazarev,[30] and Ioffe [31]—to create schools of their own.

Now, in the epoch of Socialism, when science is the base of the state's development, the influence and the importance of our scientific community are growing rapidly. We must remember that, for our science to be the world's foremost, our scientific community and its social responsibility and activity must also lead the world. This socially active community of scientists should indeed be a leading force, and an authoritative one, so that its opinions and appraisals will be recognized on a world-wide scale.

74

3a

Reminiscences about
Professor Ernest Rutherford

[*The text below is based by Dr. Kapitsa on his report delivered on November 14, 1937, less than one month after Rutherford's death, at the Institute of Physical Chemistry of the Academy of Sciences in Moscow.*]

I worked with Professor Rutherford for fourteen years, and I want to start my reminiscences with a certain episode.

This was six years ago [1931]. A congress was held at Cambridge to mark the centennial of Maxwell's birth. He was the first director of the Cavendish Laboratory, at which post he was followed by Lord Rayleigh,[1] J. J. Thomson,[2] and finally Rutherford—four scientists, four geniuses of the end of the last century and the beginning of our century. A number of Maxwell's disciples rose in the course of a solemn session with their recollections of him. Afterward Rutherford asked me how I liked those speeches. I replied:

"The speeches were very interesting, but I was struck by the fact that they said only good things about Maxwell, presenting him to us as if he were made of sugar. But I wanted to see

75

Maxwell a real, live man, with all the human characteristics and failings naturally possessed by a man, no matter how much of a genius."

Rutherford laughed and said that right then and there he was charging me with the task of telling the future generations precisely what sort of man he himself really was. Rutherford was saying this half jokingly, and I was also laughing.

And now that death has come to him so early, I speak of him, and I do want to carry out his request. But as I begin to evoke Rutherford's image to myself, so as to relay it to you, I see that his death—as well as the time elapsing since he and I last saw each other—obliterated all his little human failings. What emerges is a great man of an astonishing mind. How well do I understand now the feelings of those disciples of Maxwell who spoke then at Cambridge.

Yes, truly, in such men as Faraday, Maxwell, and Rutherford, the exceptional qualities of their mind and character eclipse completely their petty human shortcomings. When memory brings back their image, what remains is the large, the whole only.

All of us, Rutherford's disciples, were quite surprised by his death. To us he was not only immortal as a scientist—he was almost immortal also as a human. Rutherford's father and mother lived to be ninety, and Rutherford himself at sixty-six was full of strength of health, of energy—he worked days at a stretch. But an unexpected illness came, the strangulation of a hernia; an operation was necessary, following which for four days his organism fought for life, but the heart was not equal to it, and on October 19, 1937, Rutherford was no more.

Rutherford was exceptionally popular in his country; many knew him, and the mourning was nationwide. A national funeral was arranged, and the urn with his ashes was immured in Westminster Abbey, next to the tombs of Newton, Darwin, Faraday, Herschel,[3] and Kelvin.[4]

Rutherford, coming to his life's close as one of the greatest scientists of our time, was born in 1871 in the village of Brightwater, near the small town of Nelson in New Zealand. He, who was in time to become a scientist achieving all the international honors that a man of science could ever gain, began his life inconspicuously. He was the fourth child of a modest farmer in New Zealand; he was followed by eight more children. This small flax grower could not afford to give an education to his twelve children. Rutherford had to depend on scholarships from his childhood schooling to the very end of his university education.

He was a very lively, active, and cheerful child. He loved hunting and sports. At school and later at the university he played soccer as a forward. But he also loved to read, to make models, to take apart things mechanical. While still a boy he constructed a camera for himself, a rather difficult feat in those days. On finishing his secondary school in 1890, he entered Canterbury College in Christchurch. A tiny provincial school, it had only one hundred fifty students and seven professors. From the very first day he became passionately interested in science and started his researches.

During those student years at Canterbury, Rutherford was greatly attracted by the radio waves discovered by Hertz. The idea of wireless telegraph appealed to him, but the problem at that time ran head on into the question of finding a detector for the electrical oscillations caused by incoming waves. Rutherford discovered that high-frequency oscillations demagnetize iron. Practically speaking, this is very easy to ascertain if a magnetic needle is placed by the side of a magnetized cluster of iron wires put into an oscillatory circuit. In such a case the needle will perceptibly deviate as the radio waves are received. He published this discovery. At that small college this caused enough of an impression to create an immediate reputation for Rutherford.

In 1891 Canterbury's students organized a small scientific society, and at one of its meetings Rutherford—still a very young man—delivered a paper "On the Evolution of Matter." In that paper he put forth a few ideas that for the period were incredibly revolutionary: he maintained that all atoms consisted of the very same ingredients. The paper met with disapproval, and he had to apologize to the little society. It must be said that at that time, in 1891, Rutherford had no proof whatever to back up such a statement. Radioactivity was yet to be discovered—in 1896. From Dalton's [5] time on the atom had been considered as something not to be tampered with in any way at all. But the daring with which Rutherford expressed his thought, the correctness of which he would prove only twelve years later, was most characteristic of him.

He was graduated from Canterbury College in 1894, and for a year taught in a secondary school. Winning the so-called 1851 Scholarship, he left for England—for Cambridge. This scholarship, the largest prize England could give to a young student of science, guaranteed Rutherford's studies and researches for the next two or three years.

The year 1895 was a period of reforms at Cambridge. Until then, graduates of other universities had not been permitted to work in the Cambridge research laboratories. This rule was abolished on the initiative of Professor J. J. Thomson, and now graduates of other universities could continue their scientific work at the Cambridge laboratories.

Rutherford was one of the first young scientists to take advantage of the change. He enrolled in the Cavendish Laboratory, headed by Thomson. Together with him there came McClelland,[6] Townsend,[7] and Langevin.[8] All through the period of his initial stay at Cavendish, Rutherford worked in the same room as Langevin. The two became very friendly. This friendship of the two scientists beginning their work together proved to be very close; it lasted uninterruptedly till Rutherford's death.

Rutherford started out at Cambridge by continuing his radio-relay researches. He established radio connection between the laboratory and the observatory, a distance of about one and a half miles. At that time he was the first one to relay radio signals over such a long stretch. It is possible that, had he gone on with this work, he would have progressed greatly, but he was not at all attracted by the practical solution of this problem. At this point another question began to interest him—the problem of ionizing gases with the Roentgen rays, whose nature was not as yet known. He started working on this with Thomson, and the two established the phenomenon of the current of saturation during the ionization. This work, made public in 1896, may be considered as basic in this particular field.

Just at the time of these researches, in 1896, news came of Becquerel's discovery of radioactivity. Rutherford was intrigued by this phenomenon and began to study it. He was the first to show that radium emits two kinds of rays (he named them alpha rays and beta rays), differing in their capacity to penetrate matter. He demonstrated that these rays differed from ordinary rays.

In 1897 Rutherford was a young scientist already possessing a certain renown. That year he received an invitation to take the chair of physics at McGill University in Montreal in Canada. He accepted. He stayed there the ten years from 1897 to 1907. This period, spent at a small provincial university, was one of most fruitful work for him. In this there is, it seems to me, a lesson for young scientists. I hear frequent complaints from young scientists just beginning their careers that they cannot work because the conditions are not suitable, that there is no proper laboratory, that this or that is lacking. And now picture for yourself a young scientist who found himself at what he must have thought was the world's end, so far away from his native land, completely isolated from this planet's scientific community, at a place to which in those days journals came more than a month late. But this man was full of ideas, of enthusiasm. Even in that distant little corner of the world he created the most advanced, most revolutionary, most progressive views in that time's science. He attracted young scientists from all over the world; men began to come to him to be his disciples.

Rutherford's work in Canada led to a whole series of most important discoveries. First of all, he discovered the emanation of thorium. Alongside of Rutherford, there worked a young chemist named Soddy.[9] The two together began to study the chemical nature of the elements resulting from a radioac-

79

tive decomposition, for it was of great importance to ascertain the chemical as well as the physical singularities of the radioactive process. Radioactivity at that time was not as yet understood, and Rutherford and Soddy were the first to prove that this was a spontaneous transformation of one kind of element into another, a phenomenon now called radioactive decomposition. In this process, there emerge either alpha rays, consisting of fast-flying atoms of helium possessing a positive charge, or beta rays, which are fast-flying electrons. On the basis of this, Rutherford supposed that the emanation of thorium is an element differing from thorium itself. Together with Soddy, judging from its diffusion, he ascertained the atomic weight of the emanation and demonstrated that this emanation corresponds to inert gas.

A veritable revolution was caused by the theory of radioactive decomposition as formulated by Rutherford and Soddy in 1903. When, as early as 1891, while still a student, he had spoken to a students' society about evolution of matter, he had done so with no basis whatever. Now, however, when he proved this with data obtained from experiments, the resulting impression was tremendous not only in the narrow milieu of his university but among scientists everywhere. And yet, his finding was so revolutionary that many scientists, including some very important ones, did not share his view. Kelvin to the end of his life would not and did not agree that radioactivity was a decomposition of the atoms of elements. These were held by Kelvin to be the unshakable foundation of the structure of matter.

In the same year of 1903, when only thirty-two years old, Rutherford was elected to membership in the Royal Society. But this is not really so unusual for the British academy, which elects to its body a scientist just as soon as he achieves a great success in his scientific work. Thus it is not at all uncommon for young savants in the age bracket twenty-five to twenty-eight to be elected to the Royal Society. Therein lies much of the considerable strength of the Society, making it an active scientific center. This is its advantage over the academies of all the other countries.

In 1907 the chair of physics at the University of Manchester, one of England's most important universities, became vacant. In the nineteenth century this chair had been occupied by such scientists as Dalton, Joule,[10] and others. Now it was offered to, and accepted by, Rutherford. At Manchester, from 1907 to 1919, he was responsible for as important researches and accomplishments as he had earlier been at Montreal. Among his Manchester achievements we must first of all note his work on the dissemination of alpha particles as they pass through matter. This led to Rutherford's establishing a new model of the atom generally accepted to this day.

The Nobel Prize was won by Rutherford in 1908 for his work in chemistry. In 1919 he discovered the artificial disintegration of matter. He showed that not only does there exist in nature a spontaneous decomposition of radioactive elements but that also it is possible to create an artificial disintegration of the nucleus through an alpha-ray bombardment. This was discovered by him in experiments with nitrogen, and later confirmed by work with a whole series of other light elements. Thus did he create an entirely new field of nuclear physics—the artificial disintegration of the atom.

As earlier in Canada, so now at the University of Manchester, he attracted a whole galaxy of young scientists. There worked with him not only Englishmen but also Geiger [11] the German, Bohr the Dane, and others. One outstanding result after another was accomplished by his disciples in his laboratory.

Accepting the chair in experimental physics at Cambridge in 1919, he remained there the rest of his life. He succeeded J. J. Thomson as director of the Cavendish Laboratory. He continued there his work on the artificial disintegration of matter. He guided his disciples' researches. It was in his laboratory that the period's two greatest discoveries in nuclear physics were made: Chadwick's [12] discovery of neutrons, and the Cockcroft-Walton [13] work on the artificial disintegration of matter

81

under bombardment by a cluster of protons obtained in an artificial way.

Thus we see that, beginning his experiments in radioactivity in 1896, Rutherford continued them steadily until, by his life's end, this field of knowledge had assumed such proportions that it now appears to us as a separate science, that of nuclear physics.

To understand the significance of each of Rutherford's discoveries we must see clearly the historical background of all of them. But this task is too large for such an essay as this one. Yet it is most instructive to trace in a few examples the methods which were used by Rutherford in his scientific researches and which yielded him such great results.

Rutherford was an experimenter. In this he resembled Faraday. He seldom used formulae or resorted to mathematics. On occasion, while trying to illustrate a lecture with a formula, he would become confused. He would then merely write on the board his result, saying: "This is how it will look when all the calculations are right."

But he was an extraordinary master of his experiment. It may be said that he "saw" the phenomenon which he was researching, even if this phenomenon was occurring in an immeasurably small nucleus of an atom.

At the risk of oversimplification, we may discern among physicists two types of researchers. One is rather the result of the German school, wherein the experimenter proceeds from theoretical premises and endeavors to prove them through his experiment. The other type of scientist, more of the English school, proceeds not from a theory but from the phenomenon itself. He studies this phenomenon to see whether it can be explained by the existent theories. Here the study of the phenomenon, its analysis, is the experiment's main motif. If such a division into the two types is indeed possible, Rutherford was a brilliant representative of the second direction in experimental physics. With Rutherford the chief thing was to find his way, to comprehend the phenomenon. The experiment had to be structured so as to make clear the essence of the phenomenon. And so the precision and the complexity of the measurements had to fit the task of understanding the phenomenon.

As an example let me cite the case of studying alpha particles. Radium emanates alpha particles. At the very start of his experiments Rutherford showed that these are unusual rays. But what are they, really?

Rutherford decided that since they fly out of radium, they must be some or other element already in existence. To define precisely the element, it was necessary to ascertain the element's mass. And this mass had to be pinpointed with such an exactitude as would show to which one of the existing elements it corresponds.

Rutherford arranged an experiment which was quite characteristic of him. I will describe this experiment, even though it has only a historical significance, since now we use more exact and complex methods to ascertain the mass of alpha particles. Yet this initial method used by Rutherford is truly astonishing by its simplicity and its effectiveness in achieving its goal. Fig. 1 shows the instrument used in these experiments. Letter *D* indicates a simple electroscope, made from a leaf of gold foil and placed above twenty little plates of metal, *A*, all placed parallel to one another. The tolerance between the plates is only one millimeter, so as to let the alpha rays, emitted by the radioactive salt, *B* (placed at the bottom), come through as a parallel cluster into the chamber of the electroscope. To do away with the radium emanation [the gaseous substance, Radon, produced in the course of Radium's radioactive disintegration] and to increase the movement of the alpha rays, hydrogen was put through the instrument.

By applying a strong magnetic field, directed parallel to the planes of the plates, *A*, it was possible almost completely to cease the ionization in the chamber of the electroscope. In such a simple way did Rutherford show that alpha rays are particles, charged and quickly moving. By covering, from the electroscope's side, one half of the tolerances between the plates, it was possible to demonstrate that, given one direct-

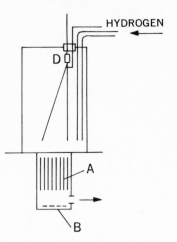

FIG. 1. Apparatus to ascertain
the make-up of alpha particles.

tion of the magnetic field, the ionization ceases at a lesser
strength of the field than when given another direction. Thus
the direction of the deviation of the alpha rays by the magnetic field was established, and thus it was ascertained that
the symbol of the charge of the alpha particles is positive. By
creating an electric field between the plates, *A*, and connecting
them in turn to the opposite poles of the battery, Rutherford
succeeded in obtaining a cessation of the ionization and a deviation of the alpha rays through an electric field. Thanks to
these data he established the speed of the alpha rays, and he
also demonstrated that the latter are a stream of positively
charged atoms with a greater mass than that possessed by the
atoms of hydrogen, in the process ascertaining—with a precision up to ten per cent—the relation of their charge to the
mass. This relation showed that the alpha particles apparently
corresponded to the twice-ionized atoms of helium.

But it was necessary to prove yet more exactly that this was
indeed helium. This work was undertaken later, in 1909, when
Rutherford was in Manchester, where he had large reserves of
radium at his disposal.

The apparatus for these experiments was also extremely simple. You see it in Fig. 2. Emanation of radium was placed into a small, thin-walled tube of glass. The walls of the tube were 0.01 millimeter thin, so that the swift alpha rays could pass through the glass while the emanation was isolated. This tube was placed into a glass vessel, *B*, which terminated in a capillary discharge tube with electrodes, *C* and *D*. By raising and lowering the mercury in the vessel, *B*, in the space surrounding this little tube, a vacuum was created. The tube with the emanation remained in the apparatus for two days, whereupon the gas, created by the passing alpha particles, was compressed by raising the mercury into the discharge tube. When lighted,

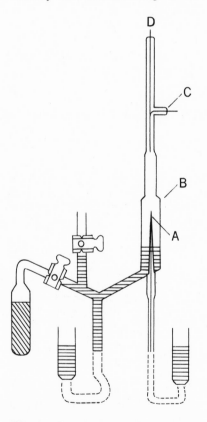

FIG. 2. Experiment confirming that alpha particles are atoms of helium.

the tube showed yellow helium lines, which proved the presence of helium. That this helium did not spread from the little tube with the emanation was easily proved by a control experiment, during which this tube was filled with helium. In such a case helium lines did not appear in the spectrum. Thus it was demonstrated that alpha rays are the atoms of helium.

The above-described experiments are extremely simple, and any student can easily repeat them. And yet these experiments, so correctly done, so directly leading to their goal, solved a question which was at that time of great importance and caused a revolution in scientists' views on matter.

But Rutherford was not satisfied with his study of the cluster of the alpha rays through observing the ionization produced by them. He searched for a method through which he could discover individual alpha particles. The very first such method was found in observing scintillations.

Already Crookes [14] had noted that, while bombarded by positive rays, certain substances luminesce. The most brightly shining substance was zinc blende. When Rutherford and Geiger placed some zinc blende under a microscope and turned a cluster of alpha rays upon it, they saw in the microscope's field of vision not an even luminescence but separate flaring dots. They concluded that the flares emerged in the places where the alpha rays struck the zinc blende. Thus it was possible to ascertain the quantity of the emanating alpha rays through the count of the flares occurring on the zinc blende.

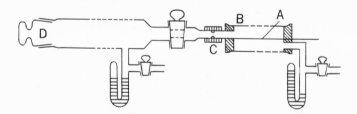

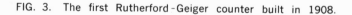

FIG. 3. The first Rutherford-Geiger counter built in 1908.

Another method originated by Rutherford to discover the alpha particles has by now become even more effective—thanks to the invention of intensified lamps—than the method of counting the scintillations. This method, based on a phenomenon discovered by Townsend, is the Rutherford-Geiger counter. If a sharp, pointed piece of metal is exposed to a gas at a reduced pressure, it is possible to choose a potential which alone prevents a discharge. If then in the surrounding gas even the weakest possible ionization of even one alpha particle is caused, a discharge at once follows and lasts for a certain period of time. This was the principle on which Rutherford and Geiger based their first counter in 1908. This is shown in Fig. 3. Instead of a sharp point, they took a tiny, thin wire, *A*, which was placed into the cylindrical vessel, *B*. Between the wire and the cylinder a critical potential was created. Through the aperture, *C*, closed by a very thin leaf of mica, alpha rays can penetrate, and their source is in the vessel, *D*. Currents discharged by the wire are registered by the stringed galvanometer, whose reactions give us a count of the alpha particles. Nowadays, the Rutherford-Geiger counter has an intensified lamp instead of a stringed galvanometer, and this makes the counter extremely sensitive. In its latest model the counter is one of the most basic instruments giving us the opportunity to do the fullest possible study of cosmic radiations.

Once he had a way of counting alpha rays, Rutherford began to study a whole series of phenomena which could not be researched before.

In 1910 his laboratory staff was joined by a young scientist named Marsden.[15] He asked Rutherford to give him a very simple assignment. Rutherford told him to count the alpha particles passing through matter and to find their diffusion. At that, Rutherford remarked that in his opinion Marsden would not find anything of note. Rutherford based this assumption on the Thomson model of the atom then generally accepted. This model showed the atom as a sphere 10^{-8} centimeters in size with an evenly distributed positive charge, into which sphere electrons were set. Harmonious vascillations of the electrons defined spectra of radiation. It was not difficult to prove that the alpha particles should pass through such a sphere easily, and any noticeable diffusion of them could not be expected. In making their run the alpha particles spent all their energy in throwing off the electrons, which ionized the surrounding atoms.

Under Geiger's supervision Marsden began to make his observations and soon found that the majority of the alpha particles did pass through matter but that there was nevertheless a noticeable diffusion, and that some particles seemed to bounce back.

On hearing this, Rutherford said: "This is impossible—as impossible as for a bullet to bounce off paper."

This phrase shows how concretely yet imaginatively he saw a phenomenon.

Marsden and Geiger published their findings, and Rutherford at once decided that the then existing conception of the atom was incorrect, that it must be radically reconsidered.

While studying the law of the distribution of the reflected alpha particles, Rutherford endeavored to ascertain the distribution of the field inside the atom necessary to find the law of diffusion wherein the alpha particles could even return. He came to the conclusion that such return is possible when the entire charge is concentrated in the center and not along the entire volume of the atom. The size of this center, which he called the nucleus, is very small: from 10^{-12} to 10^{-13} centimeters in diameter. But, then, where can the electrons be placed? Rutherford decided that the negatively charged electrons should be distributed around the center: they could stay in place thanks to gyration, the centrifugal force of which would balance the force of pull of the positive charge of the nucleus. Consequently the model of the atom is nothing else but a kind of solar system consisting of the nucleus (the sun) and the electrons (the planets). And thus did he create his model of the atom.

This model met with complete puzzlement, since it contradicted that time's seemingly unshakable foundations of physics. Rutherford of course understood that, on the basis of the Maxwellian theory, electrons while rotating around the center should doubtless radiate light, lose their kinetic energy, and sooner or later fall into the nucleus. It was exceedingly difficult at the time to go against the foundations of the Maxwellian theory. Therefore Rutherford's model of the atom was not at first accepted.

Thus two years passed. Then the young Danish scientist, Niels Bohr, came to join Rutherford's research staff. They often discussed this model of the atom. It was clear to Bohr, too, that the principles of this model's structure did not correspond to the laws which were at the time accepted as basic. And Bohr began to work on this paradox. He believed in the experimental soundness of Rutherford's model, but it was necessary to find for it a sound theory as well. The brilliant thought occurred to him to apply here the basic ideas, then just appearing, of the quantum theory of radiation. They were first advanced by Planck and considerably generalized by Einstein.

In 1913 Bohr supplied a theoretical foundation for Rutherford's model of the atom, which now is known as the Bohr-Rutherford model and serves as the basis upon which all of modern nuclear physics rests.

As he experimented, Rutherford possessed among his chief characteristics an extraordinary gift of observation, also the ability to generalize a phenomenon and to concentrate on that which was the most important and the most necessary. This may be traced through a number of examples. When, for instance, he discovered the emanation of thorium, he based this on his observation of the difference in the ionization caused by thorium when the little door of the electroscope was open and when it was closed. It seemed that the stream of air passing through the compound changed the radioactivity of thorium itself. Rutherford began to collect this air and at once discovered that it was itself radioactive. This precisely was the discovery of the emanation. Most scientists, having noticed the difference, would have started to study the phenomenon either with a closed or an open door. But Rutherford immediately posed the problem: why did this phenomenon occur so and not in some other way? And he forthwith strove to make clear to himself just what the crux of the matter was. Exactly this inevitably rising question, "Why?" contained in itself the key to great discoveries.

And here is another case. Rutherford's remarkable power of observation was demonstrated also in his discovery of the artificial disintegration of matter. The fact was that, during the observation of scintillation, it often turned out that from the matter under bombardment there flew out rays with a very long run—a much longer one than the run of the bombarding alpha particles. Everybody observed these rays and frequently spoke of them, but no one asked himself the question, "Why?" But Rutherford decided that this phenomenon must be analyzed and its essence explained. The explanation was soon found. It was proved that, under bombardment by alpha rays, the atoms of nitrogen (which is always present in the air) fall apart. This was the explanation of the long runs. Rutherford proved this with exceptionally simple experiments. Fig. 4 shows his instrument.

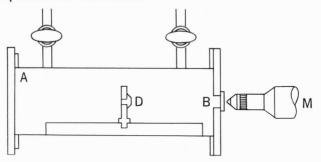

FIG. 4.   Apparatus with the help of which Rutherford carried out his artificial decomposition of elements (nuclear reactions).

The hermetic chamber, *A*, can be filled with gas through two faucets at different pressures. *D* marks the source of alpha rays; *B* indicates the screen on which we observe the scintillations with the aid of a microscope, which is marked *M*. The screen, on the side of the alpha ray source, is covered with a little plate of silver, which absorbs a considerable part of their run's energy. When filling the chamber, *A*, with nitrogen, Rutherford noticed that at a certain pressure most of the scintillations vanish. This occurs when the alpha rays, caused by the radioactive source, expend all their energy in ionizing the air and do not reach the screen. But the remaining scintillations pointed to a presence of a very small quantity of alpha rays with a run several times greater than that of the rays that came from the source. If the experiment uses not nitrogen but some other gas, such as carbon dioxide or oxygen, there are no such scintillations left. The only explanation is that they come from nitrogen. Since the energy of the remaining alpha rays is greater than that of the primary alpha rays, these remaining ones can appear only when there is a disintegration of the nucleus of the atom of nitrogen. Thus the disintegration of nitrogen was proven.

Any researcher, and not a physicist alone, cannot help but be astonished by this simplicity of the posing of the question, by this most simple experiment. Such simplicity **can come only** from a genius, particularly when it leads to such striking results.

Many say that Rutherford possessed an extraordinary gift of intuition: he sensed (as it were) just how to experiment, just what to look for.[16] Intuition usually means some sort of unconscious process occurring inside a human being; something that cannot be explained, something that—with the man himself unaware of it—brings him to the right decision. Personally I think that this may be true in part only, that in any case there is a large exaggeration in this. The average reader does not at all know the tremendous amount of work done by scientists. He learns of that portion only which leads to certain results. Observing Rutherford at close quarters, it was possible for me to see what enormous quantity of work was being done by him. His energy and his enthusiasm were inexhaustible. He worked all the time, and all the time he was in quest of something new. Rutherford published and brought to the attention of his fellow scientists only those of his works which had positive results, but these constituted hardly more than a small part of the huge amount of his labors. The rest was not only unpublished but remained unknown even to his disciples. At times, and only because of stray hints occurring in his conversation with you, it was possible to learn that he had tried something or other which had not worked out. He did not like to speak of the work he projected; he spoke more readily only about that which had already been done by him and had yielded results.

One of the brilliant examples of his exceptional perspicacity is the discovery of the neutron. The neutron is a material particle, by its mass equal to the nucleus of hydrogen, but carrying no charge. The experimental proof of the existence of such a particle was brought forth by Chadwick, a close disciple of Rutherford, at Cambridge in 1932. For this discovery Chadwick was awarded the Nobel Prize. He had been studying a phenomenon whereby the bombardment of beryllium by the gamma rays of polonium resulted in extraordinarily penetrating rays. He succeeded in proving that these were not gamma rays. This radiation had first been discovered by Bothe [17] and then researched by the husband and wife, Joliot-Curie, but only Chadwick succeeded in explaining it by proving that in this case we are dealing with neutrons. The discovery of the neutron plays a tremendous role in modern nuclear physics because the neutron is one of the basic elementary particles, of which the nuclei of all elements are built.

It turned out that already, twelve years before the discovery of the neutron, Rutherford had in great detail predicted the possibility of its existence. Here is an excerpt from Rutherford's lecture delivered before the Royal Society in 1920:

> If we are correct in this assumption it seems very likely that one electron can also bind two H nuclei and possibly also one H nucleus. In the one case, this entails the possible existence of an atom of mass nearly 2 carrying one charge,

which is to be regarded as an isotope of hydrogen. In the other case, it involves the idea of the possible existence of an atom of mass I which has zero nucleus charge. Such an atomic structure seems by no means impossible. On present views, the neutral hydrogen atom is regarded as a nucleus of unit charge with an electron attached at a distance, and the spectrum of hydrogen is ascribed to the movements of this distant electron. Under some conditions, however, it may be possible for an electron to combine much more closely with the H nucleus, forming a kind of neutral doublet. Such an atom would have very novel properties. Its external field would be practically zero, except very close to the nucleus, and in consequence it should be able to move freely through matter. Its presence would probably be difficult to detect by the spectroscope, and it may be impossible to contain it in a sealed vessel. On the other hand, it should enter readily the structure of atoms, and may either unite with the nucleus or be disintegrated by its intense field, resulting possibly in the escape of a charged H atom or an electron or both.[18]

Thus did Rutherford predict a long time in advance all those basic premises along which all of nuclear physics began to develop following Chadwick's and Joliot-Curie's discoveries.

I wouldn't call this process intuition. Rather, this is a process of deep thinking and profound experimentation. We all knew that Rutherford himself looked for the neutron. He sought it for a long time and persistently, but he did not find it where he was searching for it. In this case much depended on luck. Through theorizing it was impossible to foresee why it would be necessary to choose beryllium and polonium and not anything else. Here was a question of sheer stubborn guessing.

Rutherford was not only an extraordinarily great scientist but also an exceptional man, in the sense that he never locked himself within the limits of his laboratory—his interest embraced the whole wide world surrounding him.

93

By his appearance he was rather stocky, taller than average, his eyes light blue and always very merry, his face most expressive. He was always mobile; his voice was loud, and he just could not modulate it—he could not speak softly. When he entered the laboratory, everyone knew he had arrived, and by the intonation of his voice it was possible to judge whether he was in a good mood or not.

His entire manner of communicating with people showed, from his very first word, his sincerity and simplicity. His replies were always brief, clear, and precise. It was extremely pleasant to spend time in his company. He reacted immediately to whatever he heard from you, no matter what it was. It was possible to discuss with him any problem whatever—he would at once and willingly begin to talk about it. I recall for instance the occasion when, sipping port after a dinner, in the company of a number of scientists, Eddington [19] among others, we were talking about a meteorite that had fallen in Siberia. It had just been discovered, and we were very much interested in it. The subject was debated in all possible ways. On the basis of the data already at hand we calculated the approxiate velocity and size of the meteorite.

One of us asked: "What mathematical probability is there that such a meteorite could fall in the City, right where all the London banks are?"

We calculated the probability; it turned out to be a very small one. There were economists present. This question was raised: "What impact would there be on the British nation were the City, the banking nerve center, destroyed but the industry left intact?"

In this discussion, which lasted some two hours, everyone participated. In conversations of this kind Rutherford took the liveliest part possible.

At a sharp-witted remark from anyone Rutherford would be the first to laugh, heartily, his laughter drowning all the other voices. If he liked anything, he would speak of it immediately. There was in him no hypocrisy, no concealment of feeling. He rejoiced when, in a game, he threw the ball successfully. And it was the same joy when an experiment worked out, or a scientific award came his way. Nor did he hide his anger; you could feel at once that he was enraged. Yet Rutherford was exceptional in the way his anger would subside and his good nature prevail. Never did I see him angry for more than five or ten minutes at a time; the storm would pass quickly.

He was always most concerned about people, particularly about his staff. I was struck by the extent of this concern when I first joined his laboratory. Rutherford would not permit anyone to stay in the laboratory beyond six o'clock in the evening, and no one was allowed to work on holidays.

I protested, but he said: "It is quite enough to work up to six o'clock. The rest of the time you should be thinking. Not much good are those who work too much and think too little."

When he saw that I was fatigued, he would say immediately: "You must go away for a rest."

I objected: "Please, vacation time hasn't come yet."

He would reply, jestingly: "It doesn't matter. I will lock your room and won't allow you to work."

Later I indeed saw that the time spent resting was fully compensated for by the gained energy.

From this image of Rutherford, which I have just drawn for you, you will at once perceive a man of an unusually strong temperament. This temperament expressed itself in everything, particularly in his opinions. Rutherford could not bear any dishonesty either in work or in human relations. Were any of his students or staff members to show dishonesty, be it a misrepresentation of the results of his work or a concealment of the source of his ideas and an attempt to claim the work as his own when its idea came from another, Rutherford would lose all interest in him.

Rutherford himself was extraordinarily precise in giving credit where credit was due. When a student worked under him but did things on the basis of the student's own idea, Rutherford made sure to acknowledge that the work stemmed from the student's idea. But if the basis was Rutherford's idea, this, too, was made known by him. He felt the need to be that just.

As an example, I will cite the history of the important discovery made by his disciple Moseley.[20] He worked with Rutherford in 1912. He was then a very young man, but Rutherford always spoke of him as his best student. Moseley carried out several small but brilliant studies immediately after joining Rutherford's laboratory. He then came to Rutherford with three new ideas. One of them proved to be the theme of that very brilliant work which made Moseley's name world-famous: ascertainment of the dependence of the length of the wave of the Roentgen rays of an atom on the atom's position in the periodic system of elements. Rutherford remarked that he considered this idea the most important of the three and suggested that Moseley work on it rather than on the other two. As events were to show, Rutherford was right: this work turned out to be exceptionally important. But it was Moseley's idea, and Rutherford always made a point of saying this. (Moseley perished in World War I at the age of twenty-seven.)

These qualities made Rutherford a rare teacher who created a great school. Rutherford was just this: a teacher, not a pedagogue. When in 1894, on graduating from his university, he became a secondary-school teacher, that entire year of his teaching was an utter failure. He could not maintain classroom discipline. Noise and disorder reigned in his classes. No one understood any of his explanations of the subject. His pupils soon learned that there was really nothing to fear when, angered, he would send a student out of the room to fetch the record in which to enter the student's transgression: absorbed by his own lecture, he would not notice the offender steal back into the classroom; he would forget everything as he spoke of his subject.

In his childhood, his mother had at times charged him with looking after his little sisters; he would start reading to them, and they would slip away. To stop them from running off he would simply tie their tresses together, one little girl's hair to another girl's hair.

He lectured most excitingly, yet not all his students were pleased. Say his subject is the kinetic theory of gases, and here he comes to the problem of the clash of molecules. So he suddenly remembers the clashes of alpha particles and begins to speak of his latest researches. Now his lecture takes an entirely different direction.

When a subject interested him, his listeners were truly enchanted. Still, the students who needed knowledge for the practical aim of passing examinations did not exactly approve of Rutherford's manner of lecturing on physics. They preferred lectures that adhered to the program.

Of course a man with such tremendous enthusiasm, with such an outstanding comprehension of his subject, and with such a unique way about him could be nothing else but a great teacher. His students were carried away by him, and this made its mark at once. Already when he was quite young and researched and taught in Canada, scientists from all over the world had come to Montreal to work with him. Among others the celebrated German chemist Hahn had come. Rutherford was not yet thirty then. When he moved to Manchester, he was surrounded by a throng of disciples. There were among them Bohr, Geiger, Marsden, Moseley, Darwin,[21] Chadwick, Robertson,[22] and many others whose names are not as well known. At Cambridge, as earlier, he had numerous students, from whose midst later came excellent scientists. Of these I would name Cockcroft, Oliphant,[23] Blackett,[24] Chadwick, Ellis,[25] Henderson,[26] and many others.

Rutherford always greatly cared about his students. He would say something like this: "Should a young scientist working with me come to me after two years of such work and ask me what next he should do, I would advise him to get out of science. For, if after two years of work a man does not know what he is to do next, then such a man will not make a real scientist."

Actually he never phrased his answers that sharply. Instead he would, under some pretext or other, find for his failing students jobs in industrial laboratories or teaching positions in schools or universities.

But when a man displayed initiative and individuality, Rutherford gave him all his support and attention. And it must be said that in the process Rutherford sought every opportunity to encourage such a man's individuality. I recall an occasion, early in my work at Cambridge, when I came to Rutherford to say: "We have Mr. X with us who is working on a hopeless idea and only wastes time and equipment."

"I know," Rutherford replied. "Indeed the problem on which he is working is an absolutely hopeless one, but it is a problem he himself has thought up. Even if his experiment is not successful, it will teach him to think independently and will lead him to another problem which may not be hopeless."

He was ready to sacrifice much if only he could thereby help a man to an independence and originality of thought. When a student began to show some success and an originality of thought, he surrounded him with all sorts of care, he encouraged him in every way.

Rutherford well understood the significant role his students played in his own life and work. It was not only that they raised the scientific productivity of his laboratory. He said: "My students compel me to remain young myself."

There is a profound truth in this, for students do not permit their teacher to lag behind life, to deny everything new that is being constantly given by science. We often observe that as scientists age, they begin to oppose new theories, they underestimate new developments and directions in science. But Rutherford with readiness and good will accepted such new ideas in physics as wave and quantum mechanics, about which a number of important scientists of his generation remain to this day [1937] unjustly skeptical. This usually happens with those who do not have close disciples whom it is necessary to guide and foster.

From all I have said it is clear, it seems to me, that Professor Rutherford's death is a very heavy blow for the scientists of the entire world. Science has lost in him the greatest pioneer in research in physics since the time of Faraday. All his life, which was so fruitful with scientific discoveries, he worked on the most fundamental problems of the modern theory of the atom.

He may be regarded as the creator not alone of a new chapter in science but also of an entire new science—nuclear physics.

Already in 1896, as a very young man, he had begun to study radioactivity, which had just been discovered. From then on, his work, continuing for four decades, each year gave mankind new discoveries and new ideas, which proved to be in the vanguard in the entire world's nuclear physics.

His influence in international science greatly increased thanks to a large number of students of all nationalities, among them also several Soviet scientists, who worked in Rutherford's laboratory. His singular, self-sacrificing personality earned from them not only respect and admiration but also deep love. Thus, around him, there arose the most important school of physicists that has ever existed anywhere. And we understand readily why his death was felt by many scientists as a great personal loss.

3b

More Recollections about Rutherford

[*Address delivered by Dr. Kapitsa before the Royal Society of London on May 17, 1966. It is translated here from the Russian text printed in* Novy mir (*Moscow*), *August 1966. A different, much briefer version is to be found in* Nature (*London*), *May 21, 1966.*]

I am faced by a very difficult task, although it would seem that it is easy and simple to speak of the scientific achievements of such a great savant as Ernest Rutherford. After all, the greater the scholar's achievements the shorter and more precise their description can be. Rutherford created the modern concept of radioactivity. He was the first man to understand that this is a spontaneous decomposition of the atoms of radioactive elements. He was the first to cause an artificial disintegration of the nucleus. Finally, he was the first to define the planetary structure of atoms. Any one of these accomplishments is sufficient to make an individual a great physicist. But now these achievements and their basic significance are well known not only to college students but even to high school pupils. All of us also know those extraordinarily simple, beautiful, classic experiments with the aid of which Rutherford so convincingly made his discoveries. It would hardly be necessary to come here from the Soviet Union to tell all this to the members of the Royal Society.

It is common knowledge that out of the concept of radioactivity an independent science has by now arisen, and this is called nuclear physics. This science presently continues its ceaseless growth; of all the works now being published in all the areas of physics, one fifth relate to nuclear phenomena. Today, the field of nuclear energetics as well as the utilization of artificial radioactivity in science and technology keeps up its most rapid development. All these areas absorb the bulk of the funds being spent on science, and these sums, as is well known, are now in the billions of pounds sterling, dollars, and rubles. All this has come in the last thirty years out of that modest field of physics which was then called radioactivity and of which Rutherford is justly considered to be the founding father.

To trace this development of nuclear physics from the ideas of Rutherford and his school is an interesting and instructive task, but I am confident that such members of the Royal Society as its president, Professor Blackett, Sir James Chadwick, Sir John Cockcroft, Sir Charles Ellis, and Sir Mark Oliphant, who have come from the Rutherford school and who have made in this field their fundamental researches and discoveries, can of course speak of these problems with greater authority than I.

The only thing that I can do to satisfy the interest of the Royal Society members is to tell about Rutherford himself, as I knew him during my stay at the Cavendish Laboratory; to describe how he worked, how he molded us young scientists, and how he carried on his relations with the world of science.

Thus my task is to give you a portrait of a great scientist and an outstanding man, although this should have properly been an assignment for a creative writer and not for a scientist such as myself. But I have undertaken to do this, and mainly for the following reasons. I came to England, to the Cavendish

Laboratory, as a young man unknown to anyone, and there, in the course of thirteen years, I developed into a scientist. Those years of my work were most happy, and for my achievements I feel indebted to the steady care and attention extended to me by Rutherford not only as a teacher but also as a remarkably good-hearted and considerate man, whom I loved and to whom over the years I grew to be quite close. To address you with my reminiscences is the only way in which I can express my gratitude to this great and remarkable man.

It is well known that Rutherford was not only an outstanding scientist but also a great teacher. I cannot recall any other scientist contemporary to Rutherford in whose laboratory so many prominent physicists were formed. The history of science shows that a great scientist is not necessarily a great man, but an outstanding teacher cannot be but a great man. Thus my task is becoming yet more difficult: I am to give you a portrait not only of a scientist but also of a man. I will endeavor to make this portrait of Rutherford as alive as possible, and I will illustrate my tale with episodes which left their imprint in my memory. There are many of them, but I have chosen only those which characterize this or that side of his character. My hope is that these fragments will aid in creating Rutherford's image for you.

[Here Dr. Kapitsa repeats the episode of the congress held in 1931 at the Cavendish Laboratory when speeches in praise of Maxwell were delivered. He relates his own reaction to the "sugary" speeches, also Rutherford's laughing reply to Kapitsa, and Rutherford's request that he, Kapitsa, tell the future generations about Rutherford. This entire episode can be found at the opening of Kapitsa's address on Rutherford made at the time of the latter's death in 1937 (see pages 75 and 76 of this book).]

Much has already been said and written about Rutherford the scientist. It is generally felt that simplicity, clear thinking, great intuition, and an unusually strong temperament were the cardinal features of his creative personality. Studying Rutherford's work and observing the way he worked, you come to the conclusion that, after all, the main characteristics of his thinking were his high independence and, therefore, his daring.

The basic path of the development of the natural sciences is this: as we study natural phenomena experimentally, we incessantly check to see whether our observations correspond to our theoretical premises. Progress in our comprehension of nature occurs when contradictions arise between theory and experiment. These contradictions give us the key to a wider understanding of nature; they force us to develop our theory. The larger these contradictions the more fundamental is the reconstruction of those laws by which we explain the process occurring in nature, and on the basis of which we utilize nature for our cultural development. In science, as in history, a certain phase of development demands its genius. A certain period of development demands men of a correspondent way of thinking.

In the history of the development of physics, as in any experimental science, those moments are most interesting which compel us to reconsider fundamental scientific concepts, and for this scientists inevitably need not only brains and intuition but also a bold imagination.

To illustrate I will cite two well-known examples from the history of the development of physics which have most impressed me. The first example is Franklin's creation of the teaching about electricity. As the foundation of this teaching Franklin used the concept that electricity has a material basis: electricity soaks through metal, so to say; it can penetrate metal's solid state. We know that such a concept contradicted radically the era's concept of the solid character of matter, but it was accepted insofar as it provided a mechanism completely explaining those electrostatic phenomena which were then known. Now we know that this was borne out entirely when, one hundred fifty years later, J. J. Thomson discovered the electron. But here is the most astonishing thing in this whole story: how could it happen that Franklin, until then never occupying himself with physics, living in a small American city, far away from the centers of the world's science, a man

103

already well along in years—how could he in just a few years of his work so correctly direct the development of a whole scientific discipline? And this occurred in the middle of the eighteenth century, when science progressed thanks to practitioners of the level of Newton, Huyghens, and Euler. How could Franklin, then, achieve results which had proved to be impossible of accomplishment for professional scientists?

A similar case, when on the basis of experimentation certain fundamental concepts had to be reconsidered, involves Faraday's work on the electrical field. It is difficult to find a more revolutionary and unexpected idea than the one advanced by Faraday, according to which the electrodynamic processes should be explained by phenomena occurring in the space around the conductor. I cite this example, again, because Faraday was a scientist who lacked a systematic scientific education of the sort that in those days could be obtained at a high level even in the case of any average English scientist.

I have cited these two well-known instances to show that in science, in a certain phase of the development of new basic concepts, erudition is not the essential feature which enables a scientist to solve a problem, and that instead, the main thing here is imagination, concrete thinking, and, yet more importantly, daring. Sharp and logical thinking, which is usually characteristic of mathematicians in postulating new foundations, rather hampers scientists when it fetters their imagination.

The scientist's ability to solve major scientific problems of this kind, without demonstrating any clear-cut logical structuring in the process, is usually called intuition. It is possible that there indeed exists such a thinking process, occurring in our subconscious, but its laws are not as yet known to us. If I am not mistaken, even Freud, who dwelt on the subconscious processes most deeply, did not occupy himself with this particular problem. But if we are to define this mighty process of creative thinking as intuition, then of course both Franklin and Faraday possessed it fully. Doubtless, Rutherford was its master, too. This is why he was often called "the Faraday of our time."

When, at the very beginning of our century, Rutherford started to delve into radioactivity, his experimentation already then clearly showed contradictions vis-à-vis the law of preservation of energy, that most fundamental law of nature.

The explanation of radioactivity, first given by Rutherford as the disintegration of hitherto unshakable matter, at once gave the key to the understanding of these phenomena and moved further researches in the right direction.

The same thing happened when he created a planetary model of the atom. This model radically contradicted classic electrodynamics, since at such an orbital movement of electrons the latter should have been constantly losing their kinetic energy via radiation. But the experiment of dispersing the alpha particles, carried out in 1910 by Marsden, a disciple of Rutherford, pointed out in a well-defined way the existence of a heavy nucleus in the atom's center. So clearly did Rutherford comprehend all that was occurring at the time of the collision of the particles that to him the contradiction even with the fundamental laws of electrodynamics did not serve as a handicap to erection of the atom's planetary model. Somewhat later, in 1913, Bohr brilliantly developed the theory of the atom's structure. He did this on the basis of the then developing concepts of the quantum structure of light. Bohr's theory not only fully conformed with Rutherford's planetary model but also explained quantitatively the structure of the spectra radiated by the atom.

The singular nature of Rutherford's thinking could easily be witnessed when talking with him on problems of science. He loved to listen to accounts of experimentation. But to hold his interest it was imperative to speak about basic facts and ideas only, with no involvement in technical details, which did not intrigue Rutherford. When I happened to bring to him for his approval the blueprints of a high-powered impulse generator to obtain strong magnetic fields, he politely placed the

blueprints before him without paying any attention to the fact
that they were upside down and said: "These blueprints do not
interest me. Why don't you simply point out the principles of
this machine's function?"

He understood very quickly, from half a word, the basic
idea of an experiment. This astonished me, particularly in the
first years of my stay at Cambridge when, because of my lack
of knowledge of the English language, I spoke as yet so poorly
that I could not explain my ideas and experiments with any
clarity. Despite this, Rutherford swiftly grasped my idea and
always gave it his very interesting appraisal.

Rutherford willingly spoke of his own researches and loved
to show his installations and experiments. He liked to illustrate his talk with drawings, and for this he always kept several pencil stubs in his vest pocket. He held a pencil in a way
all his own, and it was (or so it seemed to me) a very uncom-
fortable manner—with three finger tips. He drew with a slightly
trembling hand; the drawing was simple, consisting of a small
number of strokes done with much emphasis. Quite often the
pencil's sharp end broke. He then fished another stub out of
his pocket.

Many physicists, especially theoreticians, love scientific arguments. For them, the process of arguing is a way of thinking. I never heard Rutherford argue. He expressed his view
very briefly and with the utmost lucidity and concreteness. If
there was disagreement, he listened to the objections with interest, and this is where the discussion ended.

I loved Rutherford's lectures very much and took a course
of physics which he delivered to students in his capacity as a
Cavendish professor. From this course I learned little that was
new to me, for by then I knew physics quite well, but Rutherford's approach to physics taught me a great deal. Rutherford
lectured with much enthusiasm, but while lecturing he hardly
used mathematics; instead, he usually described phenomena
with diagrams, and his talk was accompanied by clear but
sparse gestures, from which we could see how concrete yet
imaginative his thoughts were. Of considerable interest to me,

in his lectures, was the fact that he changed his themes quite frequently. His lecture's plan called for one topic, but soon, thinking in analogies, he would shift to another phenomenon, usually connected with some new experiment carried on in the field of radioactivity, and, with much absorption, he would begin to speak of what occupied him then most. At that, his assistant bore the brunt of the change: all of a sudden Rutherford would ask him to arrange a demonstration that was not in the lecture's original plan.

At Cambridge I also heard J. J. Thomson's course. As he spoke of the movement of electricity through gas, it was interesting to see how this prominent scientist approached the comprehension of nature so differently from Rutherford. If Rutherford's thought was nearer to being inductive, Thomson's thought was doubtless deductive. It seems to me that as we educate our young scientists, it is extremely useful for them to hear lectures in general courses, and these should by all means be given by outstanding scientists. Our young scientists will then learn that which they can find in no book—they will discover an original approach to the understanding of natural phenomena.

In this connection I recall a conversation I had with Horace Lamb when he told me of the time he had heard Maxwell's lectures. He said that Maxwell was not a brilliant lecturer, that he usually came to his podium with no prepared notes, and that while drawing formulae on the blackboard, he frequently made mistakes and was snagged. And when Maxwell sought and corrected his errors, Lamb learned more than from any book he had read. For Lamb, the most valuable element in Maxwell's lectures was his mistakes. There is no doubt that the errors of a genius are as instructive as his achievements.

When I was at Cambridge, Rutherford had already stopped experimenting all by himself. He worked chiefly with Chadwick and Ellis, but he always took a personal part in the experiments. The technical side of constructing the equipment for an experiment was done by a laboratory assistant. This was then Crowe,[1] whom he treated rather severely. Yet I also observed how Rutherford himself, despite the slight trembling of his hands, quite dexterously handled the little thin-walled tubes of glass filled with emanations of radium.

Although Rutherford's experiments are well known to all of you, I cannot omit saying a few words about them. The most attractive thing about them was of course the clarity in the posing of the problem—the streamlined simplicity of the methodic approach to a solution. My experience of many years as an experimenter has shown me that the best way of correctly appraising a scientist, be he a beginner or a full-fledged one, is to see—while he experiments—just what his natural bent and ability may be in seeking a simple solution. The remarkable statement by an unknown author is indeed fully valid for Rutherford: *"La simplicité c'est la plus grande sagesse."* I also wish to recall a wonderfully true and profound saying by Grigory Skovoroda, a Ukrainian philosopher. He was of peasant origin and lived in the second half of the eighteenth century. He wrote most interestingly, but in all probability, he is not known in England. He said approximately this: "We should be grateful to God that he created the world so that everything simple is true and everything complex is not true."

All of Rutherford's most splendid yet simple experiments had to do with the study of the laws of dispersal at nuclear collisions. The methods of observation of scintillation, as well as counters, were worked out by him in collaboration with Geiger in 1908. More than a half century passed, and this method-system, as well as Wilson's chamber, created at the very same time, remain as basic methods in our investigation of the nucleus and the nuclear processes. We now add only the optical and resonance methods of ascertaining nuclear moments, but in essence all of nuclear physics does not have at its disposal greater opportunities of method than those which were utilized in Rutherford's time and which, basically, were found by him and his collaborators. The modern development of nuclear physics takes place, not as a result of the emergence of new opportunities in methods to study nuclear processes, but thanks to the possibility of investigating the collision of a great number of nuclei of various elements. These clashes are now being studied at great energies mainly thanks to the construction of mighty accelerators. But even in our day the key to the knowledge of the atom's nucleus is still the method whose fundamental significance was first understood by Rutherford, and this is the study of the processes of nuclear clashes. As Rutherford used to say: "Smash the atom."

But the study of the nuclear processes at such clashes has in it to this day one great weakness: this is the necessity to use the statistical method when ascertaining the results. It is well known that one must be extremely careful in postulating a general law with the aid of limited statistical data. Someone, while discussing the use of statistics, has said: "Three kinds of lie exist: lie, bold lie, and statistics." True, this was said of the statistics dealing with social phenomena, but up to a point this may be related also to the use of statistics in physics. In no area of physics have so many crude errors and false discoveries been made as in the use of statistical data obtained as the result of nuclear collisions. To this time, almost annually, there continue to occur discoveries of new particles of elements and resonance levels which later turn out to be mistaken.

Rutherford well knew what danger lies in an unobjective interpretation of experimental data of statistical nature when a scientist wishes to obtain a certain result. In my time Rutherford considered Chadwick to be the strictest judge and severest critic in working over statistical results. Rutherford himself dealt with statistical data most cautiously, and the method he used was interesting. The count of scintillations was usually done by students who did not know just what the experiment was. The curves from point to point were drawn by persons who were not aware of the results sought. As I remember it, Rutherford and his students never made a single erroneous discovery, while at the same time there were plenty of such discoveries in other laboratories.

I did not work with Rutherford and therefore did not see him in the midst of his laboratory labors. But I know that to the end of his life he without fail devoted much time and strength to his scientific researches. And I believe that he gave not less of his attention and toil to the task of guiding your young scientists then working in the Cavendish Laboratory. The detailed guidance of them he usually entrusted to one of his senior aides. Mainly this was Chadwick. Yet he himself was interested in the choice of scientific subjects as well as in the methodical approach to the solution of the set problems. While the researcher was not as yet beginning to obtain any concrete results, Rutherford paid little heed to his work. He eschewed any petty supervision. He often visited us in the laboratory, but stayed briefly, and always asked the same question, something like: "Why are you dragging your feet? How soon will you produce results?"

When I was just beginning to work in the Cavendish Laboratory, such remarks made a very strong impression on me, especially because he pronounced them in a thunderous voice and with a stern expression on his face. Eventually I realized that these questions were merely automatic. Rutherford voiced them apparently out of habit. It is possible that he inherited this habit from the New Zealand farmers who, coming to their fields, considered it necessary to encourage the hired hands with a few strong words. I became convinced that this was indeed so thanks to the following incident, which occurred after I had worked in the Cavendish Laboratory for several years. On this occasion it was necessary for a mason to break through a solid wall, so as to lay wires for some experiment or other. This was an emergency job, but it coincided with a strike of construction workers, and finding a mason was an extremely difficult thing. Finally, success. A mason undertook the assignment, but soon he declared that he was quitting. When he was asked his reason, he replied that twice a gentleman had walked past him and both times had asked just when he would tackle the job in earnest and finish it. He was greatly offended by these remarks. On being asked who the gentleman was, the mason gave a description that made it quite clear the man was Rutherford. When Rutherford was chided, when he was told that at this particular time it was important to deal with construction workers rather delicately, Rutherford to our astonishment denied that he had said to the mason anything whatever. Apparently when he urged us not to idle in the laboratory, he was doing this in the same mechanical manner, completely unaware of his words. This was his conditioned reflex.

Rutherford's most remarkable quality as a teacher was his ability to support a scientist's start, to direct the work, and to appraise the obtained results correctly. What he valued in his pupils most was their independence of thought, their initiative and individuality. At that I must say that Rutherford used everything possible to bring the man's individuality to the fore. [Here Dr. Kapitsa repeats the story of Mr. X and his lack of success, already related in his 1937 speech (see page 98 of this book), and the tale of Moseley's success, recounted in the same speech (see page 96).]

Rutherford felt that a beginning scientist should not be given a technically difficult assignment. A scientist at the start of his career, even if he is talented, needs a success; otherwise he may suffer a needless lack of confidence in his own ability. When a student succeeds, he should be justly appraised and praised.

Once, in a frank conversation with me, Rutherford said that the main thing for a teacher to learn was not to envy his students' successes, and he confessed: "How difficult this becomes with the years!" This profound truth made a big impression on me. The teacher's uppermost quality should be generosity. Doubtless Rutherford could be generous. This apparently was the chief secret behind the fact that so many prominent scientists came out of his laboratory—that it was always possible to work freely and well in his laboratory, in its good businesslike atmosphere.

[Here Dr. Kapitsa repeats his 1937 statement on Rutherford's staying young in spirit even as he aged physically, quoting him: "My students compel me to remain young myself." Dr. Kapitsa also repeats his remarks on Rutherford's interest in such new developments as wave and quantum mechanics (see page 98 in this book).]

Rutherford was very gregarious and loved to talk with visiting scientists, of whom there were many. He was usually all-attentive to accounts of others' researches. In conversation Rutherford became animated easily. He loved jests, and himself joked often, at that laughing readily. His laughter was sincere, loud, and infectious. His face was very expressive, showing at once his mood of the moment, and whether or not he was worried by anything. His good mood demonstrated itself in his good-natured teasing of the person he was conversing with: the more he teased the friendlier he was with that person. Thus he jested in his conversations with Bohr, thus he also talked with Langevin, both of whom he loved in particular. In his merry remarks there was often more than a jest. I remember how he brought Millikan [2] to me at the laboratory, saying to me: "Allow me to introduce you to Millikan. I am sure you know who he is. Show him the installation which you use to obtain strong magnetic fields and tell him about your experiments, but I doubt if he will listen to you. He will himself start talking about his experiments." This was followed by Rutherford's laughter, in which Millikan joined, but much less heartily. Then Rutherford left, and I soon saw that his prediction was correct.

I will not dwell on Rutherford's way of delivering his scientific reports but will merely say that they always appealed to me both in their content and their form. Rutherford attached much importance to the form of a report and apparently thoroughly prepared each time. He taught me the way of reporting at the Royal Society, and I still vividly remember one of his injunctions. "Show as few slides as possible," he used to say. "When the hall is dark, the listeners take advantage of this and leave the hall."

Rutherford was interested not only in strictly scientific questions but also in much in the world around him. He read geography and history and liked to talk about the books he read. He absorbed everything with his great gusto, and he always extracted the essential things from what he read. Later, when I became a college staff member and walked him home from the Sunday dinners, we often discussed political subjects.

The very first day of my work at the Cavendish Laboratory he unexpectedly declared to me that he would not allow me to spread Communist propaganda in his laboratory. This astonished me. I was offended no less than surprised. Doubtless this was the consequence of the time's sharp political struggle and the propaganda connected with it. Until my arrival in England, while I was still in Russia, I was far distant from the events in Europe; I was so absorbed by my scientific work that the deep political hostility then existing was incomprehensible to me. Subsequently, having published my first scientific research, I presented Rutherford with a reprint of it, adding an inscription that here was proof that I had come to work with him, not to be occupied by Communist propaganda. He became very angry and returned the reprint to me. I had foreseen this and had another copy of the reprint ready with a very fitting inscription. I gave it to him. Evidently Rutherford appreciated my farsightedness, and the incident was closed. His quick temper was characteristic, but so was his ability to calm down.

Later Rutherford and I talked politics many times. In particular, Europe's rising Fascism made us wonder. Rutherford was an optimist; he felt that all this would pass. But we know that it did not turn out this way.

Rutherford, as most men of science, held progressive views.

Twice I happened to involve Rutherford in political activity of a sort. The first time this was in connection with Langevin. In his young years Rutherford had worked together with Langevin in the same room at the Cavendish Laboratory, and from the very start they had been close friends. Of course, it was impossible not to be friends with a man of such a brilliant mind and exceptional spiritual qualities as Langevin. My friends in Paris, Langevin's pupils, were indignantly telling me that Langevin, unquestionably France's greatest physicist, had not been elected to the French Academy because of his leftist views. Langevin had openly participated in left-wing organizations, was a founder of the League of Human Rights, had fought anti-Semitism during the Dreyfus case, and so on. I told Rutherford about Langevin's difficult status in France and asked him whether England was in the habit of electing, to foreign membership in the Royal Society, scientists of such leftist stands as Langevin's. Rutherford at first said something I could not understand, then began to muse what a good man Langevin indeed was, then recalled that during World War I Langevin had very actively contrived and laid an ultra-acoustic connection across the waters of the English Channel. This is where our conversation terminated. At the very next elections, in 1928, Langevin was elected a foreign member of the Royal Society, and this was many years before his election to the French Academy.

The second case occurred at the beginning of Hitler's rise. We were greatly alarmed by the fate of such prominent physicists as Stern,[3] Franck,[4] Born,[5] and a number of others in the atmosphere of the actively spreading anti-Semitism. At that time Szilard [6] visited me at Cambridge. We were faced with the problem of making it possible for these scientists to leave Germany without arousing suspicion. I turned to Rutherford, and he readily helped us, by sending his personal invitation to these physicists to come and lecture at Cambridge.

A wide range of people interested Rutherford, but he loved those humans in particular who showed their individuality. When Rutherford became president of the Royal Society, he had to attend frequent banquets and sit next to distinguished persons of the social, financial, and governmental milieus. Later he liked to tell of his conversations with them and characterize them. I remember especially what a strong impression was made upon him by Churchill. He gave a thumbnail sketch of Churchill concisely, clearly, and correctly. Above all I recall that already then Churchill considered Hitler a real danger to the world, calling him a man riding a tiger. This conversation perhaps changed Rutherford's view of the future somewhat.

Undoubtedly, Rutherford's understanding of and interest in

people—his good will toward them—were felt by the people around him. This is why his remarks, at times too blunt, and usually called tactless, were fully compensated for by his good-heartedness, his good will.

Of course, this just appraisal of people, this understanding of them, resulted from the fact that Rutherford was an excellent psychologist. He was interested in people, and he knew how to sort them out. The characterizations he gave to people were very candid and straightforward. As in science, so in this business of sizing up a man, his description of the subject at hand was always brief and most exact. Invariably I became convinced that he was right. It is possible that his approach to humans was also a subconscious process and could be called intuition.

Rutherford's understanding of human psychology and his interest in people may be confirmed by two episodes. Cambridge had a small but first-rate theater that once produced Chekhov's *Uncle Vanya*. It turned out that Rutherford attended this play and was much moved by it. As all of Chekhov's plays, this one solves a psychological problem, and at that not a simple one but one made complex by the circumstances that all the dramatis personae are deeply intellectual people, and therefore their concept of the world is very complicated. In this play a well-known professor of the humanities, as he retires, comes to his wife's estate. The estate's manager, Uncle Vanya, devotes all of himself to this job; his thought is only to get enough money for the professor. Uncle Vanya perceives that the professor is an inflated celebrity, a scholastic pedant. Against the background of this complex psychological situation, Uncle Vanya shoots at the professor but misses. I recall with what lively simplicity and lucidity Rutherford was retelling the plot to me. His sympathy was with Uncle Vanya. The fact that Rutherford was so carried away by the play shows that he loved to delve into human psychology.

I was greatly impressed by the following instance which revealed Rutherford's ability to deal with people. I think that enough years have elapsed since that time for me to tell of this case involving Paul Ehrenfest, then a very well-known physicist. Ehrenfest was born in Austria. During a mountain excursion he met a Russian woman scientist, followed her to Russia, and married her. Out there he carried out a number of important researches, mainly in thermodynamics, gaining worldwide recognition. The University of Leyden offered him a chair in physics which had just been vacated by the great Lorentz,[7] retiring because of his age, creator of the electronic theory of metals and one of the precursors of the theory of relativity. At Leyden, Ehrenfest and his home became one of the centers of the world's theoretical physics. Ehrenfest's basic quality was his unusually clear critical mind. He was not only a wonderful teacher of the young who clung to him; his criticism was considered most profound, and theoretical physicists invariably brought to Ehrenfest their major work for his evaluation. The least contradiction or error would always be spotted by Ehrenfest. It must be said that Ehrenfest criticized most readily, and he did this with great vigor, even sharply, but always with complete good will. His criticism was so earnest and fruitful that Einstein and Bohr were among those seeking it. Despite the difference in our ages, I was friendly with Ehrenfest. I frequently visited his charming, hospitable family and repeatedly listened to his scientific conversations.

His unusual critical brain did apparently hamper his imagination, and he did not himself succeed in performing work that could be considered as major. I did not know at the time that, in his heightened nervousness, Ehrenfest greatly suffered from his own realization that in his researches he could not rise to the level of the friends whose work he criticized. I learned of these sufferings early in 1933 when I received from him a long letter in which he described in detail his depression and what he felt was the worthlessness of his work. He wrote that he could not go on living. The only thing, he said, that could yet save him was to leave Leyden and his friends for as faraway a destination as possible. He asked me to help him to a job at some or other small Canadian university, through Rutherford, whom I was to request for the use of his undoubtedly large Canadian connections.

I was of course much alarmed. All of us loved Ehrenfest. We all knew his tremendous influence, as a teacher and a critic, on the development of modern physics. Translating the letter from its German into English, I brought it to Rutherford, who personally was but little acquainted with Ehrenfest. I told Rutherford that I feared for Ehrenfest's future, as the letter doubtless revealed his psychic imbalance. Perhaps, I said, this depression is only temporary, and we must help him to get rid of it. Rutherford told me not to be upset; he would take care of everything. I do not know just what Rutherford wrote to Ehrenfest, but after a while I received a most happy letter from him. He wrote that Rutherford had explained his, Ehrenfest's, role in physics and that of course he did not have to go to Canada. This whole story shows how capably Rutherford dealt with very complex psychological situations—more ably, I am sure, than even a psychiatrist could have.

Nonetheless, later in 1933 Ehrenfest's depression apparently returned, and on September 25 Ehrenfest ended his life.[8]

I recall one more case, this a merry one, typical of Rutherford's attitude toward children.

Rutherford called me to his study on one occasion, and I found him reading a letter and laughing loudly with his open and infectious laughter. The letter turned out to be from the pupils of some high school or other in the Ukraine.[9] They were informing him that they had organized a physics society and that now they intended to continue his basic work of investigating the atom's nucleus. They were asking him to become an honorary member and to send them reprints of his scientific publications. In their mention of Rutherford's discoveries and achievements in the field of nuclear physics, they used a term pertaining to physiology instead of physics. Thus, the atom's structure in the pupils' description assumed the essence of a living organism, and this was what made Rutherford laugh. I explained to Rutherford just how this distortion could have happened. Apparently, the pupils translated their letter into English themselves, using a dictionary in the process, and the Russian language—unlike English—has two meanings for its word signifying "nucleus." Rutherford said that this was what he, too, had supposed. He responded to the children with a letter in which he thanked them for the high honor of his election and enclosed reprints of his publications.

In conclusion, I wish to dwell on a question I have found discussed in literature several times. Did Rutherford foresee those enormous practical consequences of the scientific discovery and study of radioactivity? The tremendous reserve of energy concealed in matter was understood by physicists a long time ago; this comprehension proceeded apace parallel with the development of the theory of relativity. The question, not yet solved at the time, was whether man could ever find a method of realizing these huge reserves of energy. It is known that possibilities of obtaining energy through nuclear processes became increasingly actual as the understanding of the essence of the radioactive processes improved. The main problem was a lack of clarity as to the technical feasibility of effectuating these processes of energetics. I recall that when I conversed with Rutherford about this, he did not display any particular concern over this problem. From the very start of my acquaintance with Rutherford, I noticed that he had no interest whatever in technology and technical problems. It even seemed that he nursed a prejudice against them, insofar as work in the area of applied sciences was connected with money motives.

I, being an engineer by education, was naturally always intrigued by technical problems. Repeated requests came to me for advice; offers reached me to participate in the solution of technical problems in industry. When I sought Rutherford's counsel on such matters, he invariably responded: "One cannot serve both God and Mammon simultaneously." And he was right, of course.

I also remember this conversation with Rutherford at a

Trinity College dinner. I do not recall what led to it, whether it was the influence of Lombroso's book on genius and insanity or something else, but I was developing my view that any major scientist must be crazy to a certain degree. On hearing this, Rutherford asked: "In your opinion, Kapitsa, am I also crazy?"

"Yes, Professor."

"And how will you prove this?" he demanded.

"Very simply," I said. "You remember, several days ago you told me, casually, that you had received a letter from the United States with a proposal from a large American firm (I do not now recall which one, but apparently this was the General Electric Company) that you build a colossal laboratory in America and be paid a fabulous salary. You only laughed at this offer. You would not consider it seriously. Well then, from a normal man's standpoint you acted as an insane man." Rutherford broke out in laughter, saying that in all probability I was right.

In the fall of 1934, as was my custom, I left for the Soviet Union to visit my mother and friends, and was—most unexpectedly for me—deprived of an opportunity to return to Cambridge. This was the last time I saw Rutherford—in the fall of 1934. Never again did I hear his voice and laughter. For the next three or four years, in the Soviet Union, I had no laboratory of my own and could not continue my scientific work. Of course, my emotional depression was considerable. During those years the only scientist outside the U.S.S.R. with whom I corresponded was Rutherford. At least once every two months he wrote me long letters, which I deeply valued. In those letters he described the life in Cambridge, spoke of his scientific successes and his school's achievements, wrote about himself, joked and gave me advice, invariably bolstering me up in my difficult situation. He well understood that my chief desire was to return to my scientific work, which had been so sharply interrupted. It is well known that only thanks to his concern and aid was I finally able to get my scientific equipment from the Mond Laboratory, so that three years later I could again resume my researches in the field of physics of low temperatures.

I am confident that Rutherford's letters will in time be published, but in the meanwhile I would like to cite a few excerpts from them. These speak for themselves.

On November 21, 1935, he wrote:

> I am inclined to give you a little advice, even though it may not be necessary. I think it will be important for you to get down to work on the installation of the laboratory as soon as possible, and try and train your assistants to be useful. I think you will find many of your troubles will fall from you when you are hard at work again, and I am confident that your relations with the authorities will improve at once when they see that you are working wholeheartedly to get your show going. I would not worry too much about the attitude or opinions of individuals, provided they do not interfere with your work. I daresay you will think I do not understand the situation, but I am sure that chances of your happiness in the future depend on your keeping your nose to the grindstone in the laboratory. Too much introspection is bad for anybody!

On May 15, 1936, he wrote:

> This term I have been busier than I have ever been, but as you know my temper has improved during recent years, and I am not aware that anyone has suffered from it for the last few weeks!
>
> Get down to some research even though it may not be of an epoch-making kind as soon as you can and you will feel happier. The harder the work the less time you will have for other troubles. As you know, a reasonable number of fleas is good for a dog—but I expect you feel you have more than the average number!

He gave his beautiful fatherly counsels briefly, clearly, and with spirit. His last letter was dated October 9, 1937. He wrote in detail about his proposed journey to India. The letter contains one phrase which I want to quote: ". . . I am glad to say that I am feeling physically pretty fit, but I wish that life was not quite so strenuous in term-time . . . ."

Ten days before his death he did not realize how close his end was.

To me Rutherford's death was not only the loss of a teacher and a friend. To me, as for many other scientists, it was also the end of a whole epoch in science.

Apparently those were the years of the beginning of that period in the history of civilization which is now commonly called the scientific-technical revolution. One of the main factors of this revolution is mankind's utilization of nuclear energy. We all well know that the consequences of this revolution may be very terrible: it may destroy mankind.

Although we all hope that men will have enough brains finally to turn the scientific-technical revolution to the right path toward mankind's happiness, yet, in the year of Rutherford's death, we saw the departure with no hope of return of that happy and free scientific activity which we so enjoyed in the years of our youth. Science has lost its freedom. It has become a productive force. It has become rich, but it has also become a prisoner, and part of it is veiled. I am not sure whether Rutherford would have continued in our days to jest and laugh as before.

[The version of Dr. Kapitsa's speech at the Royal Society as reported in the London *Nature* ends in a notable sentence which is absent from the version as published in the Moscow *Novy mir*. Here it is:]

In 1921 Rutherford warned me not to make any Communist propaganda in his laboratory, but it now appears that just at that time he himself together with his pupils was laying the foundations for a scientific-technical revolution.

3c

The First Two and a Half Years with Rutherford—Young Kapitsa Writes to His Mother

[*These letters appear on pages 504-519 of Daniil S. Danin,* Rezerford *(the Russian transliteration and pronunciation of Rutherford's name), a biography of Dr. Kapitsa's mentor and friend, issued in Moscow in 1966 by* Molodaya gvardiya *(Young Guard), the publishing house of the Central Committee of the Communist Youth League (Komsomol), in its series "Lives of Remarkable People." On page 611 Danin reveals that Dr. Kapitsa was among his sources for this biography of Ernest Rutherford. Presumably Dr. Kapitsa's letters to his mother came to Danin, for inclusion in his book, from Dr. Kapitsa himself. In a shortened version, these letters also appeared in Daniil Danin's "Nachalo bylo daleko" (The Beginning Was Distant), published in the Moscow monthly magazine* Yunost' *(Youth) for October 1966. Frequent dots as used by Danin in the text of the letters show that he omitted some of the text but how much we have no way of knowing.*]

The First Two and a Half Years with Rutherford

London, July 13, 1921.
IN all likelihood I will remain here for the winter. I will live in Cambridge and work with Professor Rutherford. He gave his consent; we [1] visited him yesterday. Our mission has also agreed to leave me here. . . . How will you, out there, get along without me? I do not know whether or not I am to rejoice. . . . On the other hand, I won't be able to work through the winter.[2] After all, my work and you, my dear ones, are all I have in life.[3]

London, July 15, 1921.
. . . You darling will miss me, but please don't. I, too, will find it difficult to stay here without you, but my work must go on. My youth will fly by, and nothing will bring it back. I am now worried about my work in Cambridge, how it will go, just how well I will be able to work with Rutherford, what with my weak knowledge of the English language and my rather crude manners. I will travel to join him on July 21. . . .

Cambridge, July 24, 1921.
[All the subsequent letters are from Cambridge.]
. . . I have moved from London to Cambridge and have begun to work at the laboratory. . . . For the time being I am getting acquainted with radioactive measurements and am simply occupied in my practicum; [4] as to the future, I don't know. I plan nothing, and I don't try to guess the future. What is to come will come. . . .

July 29, 1921.
. . . It is good to work here, although so far I have not been doing any independent research. . . . My feeble knowledge of the language hampers me in the expression of my ideas. Even in Russian I express my thoughts poorly. . . .

August 6, 1921.
. . . I have been in Cambridge more than two weeks already. . . . Now comes the riskiest moment—selecting a topic for my

research. Not an easy matter. . . . When such moments come to me, I don't like to say much, and therefore it is difficult for me to write anything definite. . . .

August 12, 1921.

. . . Yesterday for the first time I had a conversation with Professor Rutherford on a scientific subject. He was very pleasant, took me to his room, and showed his equipment. This man certainly has a kind of charm, although at times he is rude. And so my life flows here, like a river with neither whirlpools nor waterfalls. . . . I work until six. After six I either read, or write letters, or go riding on my motorcycle. This is my great pleasure. . . .

August 16, 1921.

. . . Everything was going very well, although we [5] were not riding slowly. But suddenly . . . an accident happened to us. . . . There are now six bruises and scratches on my body. . . . The main thing is my mug. You should see it! One half is exactly as thick as the other, and in addition there are blotches of congealed blood. I was very much ashamed to show myself at the laboratory on Monday. . . . But a pal explained to me that, at Cambridge, men are not ashamed of such physiognomies. To the contrary, this is considered a kind of particular chic, so much so that it immediately evokes respect and awe (this is, of course, if such a physiognomy is a result of engaging in some sport and not a consequence of a drunken brawl). When I arrived at the laboratory, I was of course a minor sensation. . . . I will be considerably more careful from now on. . . .

September 18, 1921.

. . . Don't I again begin to try things that are too large-scale? I am planning big things. . . . And then, this very same Rutherford is an enigma. Will I be able to solve it?

The First Two and a Half Years with Rutherford

October 7, 1921.

. . . I am now working in a big room, where several more men will work, too. So far I know one Japanese,[6] also an American will work here; [7] a motley company, as you see. This place (the Cavendish Laboratory) is being visited by various scientists all the time. . . . Today Professor Langmuir [8] from America delivered here a lecture on the structure of the molecule. The lecture led to a lively debate in which Rutherford, Thomson, Darwin, and Perrin [9] participated. They did not show too much sympathy for Langmuir's theory; they pushed him around somewhat. An analogous theory, stated by Bohr, the Danish physicist, is preferred here. . . .

October 21, 1921.

. . . Rutherford is increasingly pleasant to me. He greets me with a bow when he sees me and inquires about the progress of my research. But I am a little afraid of him. I work practically next to his study. This is bad, since I must be careful about my smoking: should he see that pipe in my mouth, there would be trouble. But thank God, he is heavy-footed, and I can tell his steps from those of others. . . .

October 25, 1921.

. . . My relations with Rutherford, or Crocodile,[10] as I call him, are improving all the time. I work diligently and with enthusiasm.

November 1, 1921.

. . . Don't worry about me—I am, as they say, "all right." [11] The results so far accomplished by me are already such as to give hope for a positive outcome of my experiments. Rutherford is satisfied, as his assistant has told me. This can be seen in his attitude toward me. He always says friendly things to me when he meets me. This past Sunday he invited me to a tea in his house, and so I observed him at home. He is very charming and simple. He asked me questions about Abram Fyodorovich [Ioffe]. But . . . when he is displeased, hold onto your seat. He will cuss you out the worst way ever. But what an astonishing cranium! His mind is absolutely unique: a colossal sensitivity, intuition. I have never been able to imagine anything like it in existence. I am attending a course he is giving, also his reports. He states his subject very lucidly. He is a completely extraordinary physicist and a very singular personality. . . .

November 9, 1921.

. . . As before, I am enjoying my work. I am taking a course of lectures, given by Rutherford himself, on the latest successes in experiments with radium. He lectures wonderfully well, and I greatly enjoy his manner of tackling and analyzing matters. . . . But he is so very ferocious that at times I am frightened, and yet I am not naturally timid. . . .

November 21, 1921.

. . . I must increase the sensitivity of my equipment ten to fifteen times at least, and I have already reached a level of sensitivity in excess of the usual level reached by equipment of this type. . . . Crocodile often comes to see what I am doing. On his latest visit, inspecting my curves, he remarked that I was already near the set goal. But the closer you come the more and more difficulties there are. . . .

December 5, 1921.

. . . As usual, I am working full speed ahead. Therefore I feel fine. . . . You know, when a professor visits you, this is considered an event, and Crocodile came to see me some five or six times in the last three weeks. . . .

December 16, 1921.

. . . Vacation time is coming soon, and the laboratory will close for two weeks. I asked Crocodile's permission to continue working, but he declared he wanted me to rest because every human being must rest. He has astonishingly improved in his attitude to me. Now I am working in a room of my own—this is a big honor here. . . . A comical thing occurred, which must

126

be described: a dinner of the Cavendish Physics Society. Members are males only, and one becomes a member automatically if one works at the laboratory. . . . There are usually thirty to thirty-five diners. . . . We sat at a table that had a horseshoe shape. One of the young physicists was chairman. . . . We didn't really drink much, but Englishmen get tipsy quickly. And their faces at once show this. They become mobile and lively; they lose their stoniness. After the coffee, port was served, and toasts began. The first one to the King. The second to the Cavendish Laboratory. . . . The toasts were supposed to be as funny as possible. These Englishmen greatly love to jest and joke. . . . Between the toasts, songs were sung. . . . In general, one can do at the table anything he pleases: one can squeal, shout, and so on. All this had a rather wild aspect, yet very picturesque. After the toasts, all present mounted their chairs, held hands in a crisscross manner, and sang a song in which they recalled all their friends. . . . It was very amusing to see such world-famous men as J. J. Thomson and Rutherford standing on chairs and singing at the top of their voices. . . . At midnight everyone went home, but I reached my rooms only at three o'clock in the morning, for there were among the diners such as had to be taken to their homes. I assure you that I was among those who were taking others home and not among those being taken. And this is rather more pleasant. Evidently my Russian belly is geared to alcohol better than an English one. . . .

December 22, 1921.

. . . Today at last I achieved the long-awaited deviation in my apparatus. Crocodile was very pleased. Now the success of the experiments is almost guaranteed: there are as yet a few difficulties, but I think I will overcome them. . . . Should these experiments succeed, I will accomplish the solution of a problem which, beginning with 1911, neither Crocodile nor Geiger, another good physicist, could solve. I won't try to explain these experiments to you—you will anyway understand nothing; I will only say that the apparatus built by me is called a microradiometer, and I have so perfected it that I can see the flame of a candle placed at a distance of two versts from my apparatus.[12] It is sensitive to one millionth of a degree! With the aid of this apparatus I measure the energy of rays emanated by radium. Tomorrow I am going to London, since our Christmas vacations are starting and the laboratory is closing. . . .

January 3, 1922.

. . . I am so used to working that the recess does not bring me any pleasure. But Rutherford, having noticed that I was overfatigued, advised me to take a trip, to rest. . . .

January 17, 1922.

. . . The fact is that one Sunday I went on a motorcycle ride, taking Chadwick along; he is one of the local young scientists. I was foolish enough to put him in the driver's seat, and as a result he, at a fast clip, sent the machine tumbling, and both of us were thrown out. . . . Despite the fact that I had a high temperature and my head was so bandaged that my nose alone was visible, I did not interrupt my work in the laboratory. Crocodile tried to send me to bed, but I won't go. By the way, he was most attentive to me. All this has proved to my advantage. . . .[13]

February 3, 1922.

. . . I am now busy with lectures and reports, and our people pile me high with work: I must help some of them with their calculations, I have to aid others to build their equipment. . . . I am now in a happy mood, for my work progresses quite successfully. . . .

February 5, 1922.

. . . Last trimester I worked fourteen hours a day, but now all I can do is eight to ten hours. . . .

The First Two and a Half Years with Rutherford

February 16, 1922.

. . . Today I had a talk with Rutherford. . . . You won't believe what an expressive mug he has—it's sheer delight. He called me to his office. We sat down. I looked at his physiognomy, and for some unknown reason I felt like laughing, so I started to smile. Imagine, Crocodile's mug also dissolved into a smile, and I was ready to burst out laughing when I remembered that I must behave respectfully, so I began to make my report. . . . Later, seeing that he was in a genial mood, I spoke to him about one of my ideas. This idea has to do with delta radiation, whose theory is very unclear. I gave him my explanation. A rather complicated mathematical calculation confirms this idea well; it explains a whole series of experiments and phenomena. Until then, whoever had heard this from me had found my suggestions too daring and regarded them most skeptically. Crocodile, in that lightning-quick way so inherent in him, grasped the essence of my idea and, imagine this, approved it. He is a blunt man. If he happens to dislike something, he will cuss so that you don't know where to hide. But here he praised my idea highly and advised me to start the experimentation to prove my theory. He has a devilish intuition. Ehrenfest in his latest letter to me calls him simply a god. Rutherford's positive opinion has encouraged me mightily. . . . It's very amusing here: if the Professor is pleasant to you, everyone else in the laboratory is affected—they also become attentive to you. . . . I am not timid, but I lose my nerve before him. . . .

March 2, 1922.

. . . All that I have accomplished . . . is simply this: from a zero I have become an ordinary staff member, who is no worse and no better than anyone of the other thirty persons working at the Cavendish Laboratory. . . .

March 13, 1922.

. . . Crocodile is as charming to me as before. At times he is even touching in this. . . .

Four Men of Science

. . . Crocodile is satisfied, and he and I already converse about my future researches. It was most amusing today. As I have already written to you, my work was begun several years ago by Crocodile himself and then [continued] by the German scientist Geiger, but because of the lack of finesse in their methods neither one of them could investigate this phenomenon through to its end, which I have now succeeded in doing. . . . It turned out that my data are more closely conforming to those of Geiger, but not those of Rutherford. When I informed him [Rutherford] of this, he calmly said to me: "This is how it should be: Geiger's work was done later, and he worked under more favorable conditions." This was charming of him. . . .

April 7, 1922.

. . . By Crocodile's special permission, I worked after our closing time. Later, coming home, I kept on calculating my results till four or five o'clock in the morning, and soon afterward began everything again in the laboratory. I am somewhat fatigued. . . . Lately I have had three long conversations with Crocodile (an hour each time). It seems to me that he is now well disposed toward me. But I am rather scared—he pays me altogether too many compliments. . . . He is a man of a strong and unbridled temperament. And such men are always known for their sharp changes of mood. But, dear mother, his head is indeed astonishing. He is bereft of any and all skepticism; he is bold, and [in his work] is carried away passionately. It is no wonder that he can make thirty men work. You should see him when he cusses. . . . Here is a sample of his talk:

"But when will you get results?"

"How long will you be dragging it out so senselessly?"

"I want results from you, results, and not your babbling. . . ."

And so on.

By the might of his mind he is placed on the same level with Faraday. Some place him even higher. Ehrenfest writes to me that Bohr, Einstein, and Rutherford occupy the very first place among the physicists sent to us by God. . . .

The First Two and a Half Years with Rutherford

May 24, 1922.

. . . Again I work like an ox, not less than fourteen hours a day. . . . I intend to write my piece next week and send it for publication. Crocodile is hurrying me.

June 15, 1922.

. . . They say that my piece has come out all right. It has been translated and is now being retyped. It will be ready tomorrow, and the day after tomorrow I will perhaps hand it to Crocodile. . . . I am a little worried. . . . I have begun new work with a certain young physicist.[14] Crocodile is taken with my idea and thinks that we will succeed.[15] He has a devilish sense for experiment, and if he thinks that there will be a good result, this is a very good omen. His attitude toward me gets better and yet better. . . .

June 19, 1922.

. . . Today Crocodile summoned me twice in connection with my manuscript. He had read it, changed it in several places, and, having done so, called me. . . . It will be published in the proceedings of the Royal Society (something like our *Izvestiya* of the Academy of Sciences)—which is the greatest honor that a piece of research can merit here. . . . Certain of the phenomena which I describe have been observed for the first time. Today Crocodile wanted by all means to insert mention to the effect that these phenomena were observed for the first time. I declined his suggestion. I have never before been so excited. I proposed, even if cautiously, two hypotheses, and I greatly fear for their fate. When just chatting in the company of my friends, I do not feel any special responsibility. But here, when I come out before Europe's market [scientific community], I feel frightened and vulnerable. Crocodile "ordered" me to write an "abstract" of my work, which will be read at a session of the Royal Society. Today I brought it to him. He was not satisfied with it. And he wrote one for me. The care with which he went through my manuscript touched me to the depth of my soul. . . . Only now have I really entered Crocodile's school

. . . and feel I am in the center of this group of young physicists. This is without doubt the world's most advanced school, and Rutherford is the world's greatest physicist and organizer. . . . Only now have I for the first time begun to feel my strength. Success gives me wings, and I am carried away by my work. . . .

July 5, 1922.

. . . I have already written to you that I decided on a new piece of research, of a very daring and very risky nature. I was much worried. The first experiments miscarried. Tomorrow's experiments should yield a final result. But Crocodile is placing one more room at my disposal and agrees to the expense. . . .

July 6, 1922.

. . . We in Russia used to pattern everything on the German model, and we had little in common with England's scientific world. I do not recall a single Russian physicist working in England any length of time. But England has produced the greatest physicists, and now I am beginning to understand the reason: the English school develops individuality on an extraordinary scale; it gives limitless room for a personality to show itself. Rutherford does not press a man; he is not as demanding about precision and polish of results as Abram Fyodorovich [Ioffe] is. . . . Here they often do research so absurd in its ideas that in our country they would have been simply laughed out of court. When I inquired as to the reason this research had been started at all, I learned that these were young men's ideas, and Crocodile values a man's initiative so much that he not only permits the man to work on his own subjects but at times even encourages him and tries to put some sense into these schemes, which are sometimes absurd. The absence of criticism, which undoubtedly kills individualism, of which [criticism] Abram Fyodorovich has an excess, is one of the phenomena characteristic of Rutherford's school. The second factor is the striving to obtain results. Rutherford is very much afraid that a man may work without achieving results, since he [Rutherford] knows that this may kill the man's desire to work. Therefore he does not like to give a difficult assignment. When he does give such a hard task, this means that he simply wishes to get rid of the man. In his laboratory it just could not happen to me that I would toil for three years over one piece of research, struggling against difficulties beyond my capability. . . .

Sometime in July, 1922 [*the exact date not specified*].
. . . I will try to explain to you my situation, in general terms. Imagine a young man who arrives at a world-renowned laboratory situated at England's most aristocratic and conservative university, where royal children are being educated. And so this young man is accepted at this university, he who is known to nobody, who speaks English poorly and carries a Soviet passport. Why was he accepted? To this day I do not know. Once I asked Rutherford about this. He laughed heartily and said: "I was surprised at myself when I agreed to accept you, but anyway I am very glad that I did this. . . ."

July 14, 1922.
. . . Crocodile is not at the laboratory. He has been in Tyrol some three weeks. He will come back tomorrow. I am awaiting him impatiently, to share my success with him. He is always so receptive to this.

July 30, 1922.
. . . Abram Fyodorovich has arrived in London. He later came to Cambridge to see the laboratory. Rutherford received him well, inviting him to dinner. . . . I joined them at dinner. We played ball after dinner. Rutherford, Fowler,[16] and I made up one team; Taylor,[17] Aston,[18] and Abram Fyodorovich the other. We won. . . .

August 17, 1922.
. . . The preliminary experiments . . . ended in a complete suc-

133

cess. I was told that all Crocodile could talk about was only them. I was given new large space, this in addition to the room in which I work, and for this full-scale experimentation I received permission to spend a rather large sum. . . .

September 2, 1922.

. . . My experiments are assuming a very large scale. . . . I will remember my most recent conversation with Rutherford as long as I live. After a whole string of compliments, he said to me: "I would be very glad if I had an opportunity to create here for you a special laboratory where you could work with your students." (Two Englishmen are now working under me.[19]) . . . Judging from the generosity with which he appropriates money for me, and from the attention he gives me, this is possibly not just a phrase. He has already placed two rooms at my disposal. Am I indeed such an able man? I am afraid; I shiver in my boots. Will I manage it all?

October 18, 1922.

. . . I feel I am a member of a collective headed by Crocodile. I feel I am indeed turning one of the little wheels of European science.

October 22, 1922.

. . . I made a small error in a technical detail of an apparatus. When I told Crocodile of this, he said to me: "I am very glad that you have erred at least once." You see, he is quite a hand at uttering compliments, since in fact I do err very often. . . . Rutherford is really, extraordinarily, good to me. Once, in a bad mood, he told me that I must economize. I argued back that I was doing everything at a very low cost. Of course he could not deny this and said: "Yes, yes, this is all true, but it is my duty to tell you this. Bear in mind that I spend more money on your experiments than on the experiments of the rest of the laboratory put together."

And you know, this is true. Our installation has cost him quite a pretty kopeck. . . .

The First Two and a Half Years with Rutherford

November 8, 1922.

. . . Now Crocodile. . . . The most comical thing is that he, just as Abram Fyodorovich, calls me over after a report or a lecture of his, when of course there is no one around, and asks: "Well, what did you think of it?" He very much loves to be praised, and it is true, he is always brilliant. Yet I try to criticize him, but in such a way that he wouldn't be offended. After all, dear mother, he is the world's greatest physicist! Yesterday he and I talked for ninety minutes or two hours about a certain idea which he expressed in his latest lecture. . . . You know, my dear, I am not too clear a speaker. My thought makes big illogical jumps, and few people understand me quickly. Abram Fyodorovich was one of them. Also Kol'ka.[20] But Crocodile undoubtedly beats the record, if we take into account my poor knowledge of the English language. And yet, despite this, I am not certain that his good will toward me will last. He is a very temperamental man, his mood swinging far, now in one direction, now in the opposite one. By this time I know his character quite well. Since his room is across the hall from mine, I hear him when he closes the door. And the way he closes it tells me his current mood almost precisely. . . .

November 29, 1922.

. . . For me today is a historic day, to a certain degree. . . . Here a photograph lies before me—there are just three distorted lines on it. But these three distorted lines are a flight of alpha particles in a magnetic field of terrific force. These three lines have cost Professor Rutherford one hundred fifty pounds sterling, and their cost to me and to Emil Yanovich [21] was three and a half months of hard work. But here they are, and everyone at the university knows and talks about them. Strange: only three distorted lines! Crocodile is very pleased with these three distorted lines. True, this is only a beginning of my research, but already from this first photo a number of conclusions can be drawn, conclusions which until now were either not even suspected or could be guessed by circumstantial evidence only. Many people have come to my room at the laboratory to see these three distorted lines and to admire them. But I must work on and on. There is much toil ahead of me. Crocodile called me today to his office and discussed further plans with me. . . .

December 4, 1922.

. . . These days I feel a kind of celebrity. On Saturday the 2nd there was a reception at Professor J. J. Thomson's for the Dutch physicist Zeeman,[22] who had just arrived. . . . Of course, I had to force myself into my evening suit. I talked with Zeeman, and I was introduced approximately in this way: Here is a physicist who solves such problems as are considered impossible [of solution]. And these mighty ones buttonholed me for nearly twenty minutes until I slipped away into a corner. . . . Today Zeeman and Lord Rayleigh (son) [23] visited me at the laboratory and looked at my work. . . .

January 27, 1923.

. . . On Wednesday I was elected to the University, and on Friday I was accepted a member of [Trinity] College. They made certain exceptions for me, and, it seems, within five months I can receive my degree of doctor of philosophy. . . . (All was arranged of course by Crocodile, whose goodness to me is simply limitless. . . .)

February 18, 1923.

. . . How everything has changed! How strange it is to look back. . . . Such care as I now see from Crocodile I have not as yet seen from any other patron. . . .

March 18, 1923.

. . . I am afraid that you have a wrong impression of my status here. The matter of fact is that my life in this wide world is not at all sweet. I am overflowing with anxiety, struggle, and toil. . . . The circle which I have organized takes a lot of my strength.[24] . . . The only thing that lightens my work is

The First Two and a Half Years with Rutherford

Crocodile's care for me, such care as can be clearly compared to that from one's own father. . . .

March 25, 1923.
. . . You are asking me to send Crocodile's photo to you. . . . Crocodile is a dangerous animal, and it is not so easy to photograph him. . . .

April 14, 1923.
. . . The main work has been completed and has produced dazzling results. . . . The scale of my work is now large, and this always frightens me. But the fact that Crocodile is backing me inspires me with daring and confidence. My dear, you cannot imagine what a great and remarkable man he is.

June 15, 1923.
. . . Yesterday I was made a doctor of philosophy. . . . Achieving this rank has cost me so much that I am nearly destitute. It is a good thing that Crocodile has lent me some money and I will be able to go away for a rest. . . . Here is what has happened to me here. This year the Maxwell stipend is offered. It is awarded for three years to the best of all those working in the laboratory, and the winning of it is considered a great honor. . . . On Monday, which was the last day to file applications, Crocodile called me to his office and asked why I was not filing. I replied that I considered my salary adequate and, besides, being a foreigner and a guest, I should be modest. . . . He said that my foreign origin was in no way a bar to getting such a stipend. . . . For me, bird of passage that I am, this [honor] is of course of no consequence whatever. But Crocodile apparently could not comprehend my psychology, and we parted rather stiffly. . . . Apparently my refusal somewhat puzzled and offended him. . . . Despite this, I am sure that I behaved correctly. Yet I am also rather bothered by a feeling that I offended Crocodile, who is so infinitely good to me. . . . But, evidently, all will end well.

Before his departure (he has left for a month's rest) I met him in the hall. I was just then returning from the ceremony of becoming a doctor. I asked him, bluntly: "Don't you find, Professor Rutherford, that I look wiser?"

"Why should you look wiser?" He was intrigued by my unusual question.

"I have just become a doctor," I replied.

He immediately congratulated me, and said: "Yes, yes! You do look considerably wiser, and at that you have gotten a haircut," and he laughed.

Taking such liberties with Crocodile is generally very risky, because in most cases he sends you straight to the devil, and, it seems I alone of the entire laboratory [staff] take a chance with such stunts. But when they come off all right, this shows that our relations are all right. In general I must have stumped him with such pranks quite a few times. At first he is at a loss, then he sends you to the devil. Such an attitude toward him on the part of a junior is all too unusual. Some six times in the past, it seems, I have heard such compliments from him as "you fool," "jackass," and the like. But by now he is somewhat accustomed to me. Still, most of the personnel at the laboratory are puzzled as to how, generally, such little tricks as mine are possible. But I am terribly amused when Crocodile is so stumped that as a first reaction he cannot utter a single word. . . .

July 23, 1923.

. . . Crocodile offered me the very stipend.

I surrendered and filed an application. . . . This prize will be very handy. . . .

August 23, 1923.

. . . I am awarded the Clark Maxwell Prize, and with it many congratulations have come.

August 30, 1923.

. . . I am starting new experiments along a most daring line.[25] If this time, too, I am lucky, it will be very good. Last evening

I was at Crocodile's house, discussed some of these questions, stayed for dinner, and we talked a great deal on various topics. He was very pleasant and showed much interest in my experiments. I must have spent some five hours with him. He gave me his portrait. I will take a photo of it and send it to you.

October 4, 1923.

. . . I am given a large room in the laboratory which has been remodeled especially for me. The remodeling was completed the day before yesterday, and we moved into this room (rather, three rooms!!). It is an excellent place. . . . I am sending Crocodile's photograph to you.

October 21, 1923.

. . . The meetings of our circle, of which I am the initiator, are also a relaxation. This moves along very well; our discussion is very free. Now, at the Cavendish Laboratory, Crocodile is also planning a colloquium.

December 18, 1923.

. . . Crocodile says that I should continue working here for some five years more, and afterward I could myself dictate terms, should I wish to move to another place. This is of course quite something, coming from him, but I am afraid that he is exaggerating.

4

Paul Langevin, Physicist and Civic Leader

[*This address was delivered by Dr. Kapitsa on January 23, 1957, at a combined session of the Soviet Academy of Sciences and the Friendship Society in Moscow, to mark the eighty-fifth anniversary of Langevin's birth.*]

Paul Langevin was not only an outstanding physicist but also a prominent civic leader in the cause of progress. He was a great friend of the Soviet Union. In 1924 he was elected a corresponding member of the Soviet Academy of Sciences, and in 1929 he was chosen an honorary active member of the same Academy. He was an honorary member of various academies and scientific societies in a number of other countries as well. Thus in 1928 he was awarded an honorary membership in England's Royal Society; and in 1934, in the French Academy of Sciences. He earned these honors as a physicist who contributed exceptionally important scientific works.

His basic contributions are in theoretical physics, most significantly in magnetism, where his research to this day has significance and is considered classic, and also in acoustics.

Paul Langevin, Physicist and Civic Leader

Langevin discovered the method of bringing forth supersonic waves and was the first to propose the use of the phenomenon of the piezoelectric crystal to excite brief acoustic oscillations. By now, on the basis of this, there has emerged a whole field of science and technology.

It must be said that Paul Langevin's influence in the development of world physics was very great and was not limited to these two areas of magnetism and acoustics. Langevin was also a marvelous teacher; he had many disciples, two of whom—de Broglie [1] and Joliot-Curie [2]—received world-wide recognition.

Although Langevin's publications were comparatively few, he was nevertheless a most generous teacher, suggesting research ideas to his students, inspiring and helping them. In this respect his influence in French physics (if this could be measured) was surely not lesser but actually greater than the influence of his publications.

I met Langevin quite frequently, and I was fortunate to win his friendship. I now recall him with a particularly warm feeling.

It may be possible to characterize Langevin concisely, I think, by saying that he was a man who served the cause of progress in everything he did. He was a man of progress in science, in his political views, in his philosophical attitudes, and in his civic activities. This cause of progress is a most prominent thread in the fabric of his life. Mankind is growing more civilized, science marches forward, the social structure of humanity is developing apace, and our philosophical concepts of man's relation to the material world surrounding him are becoming deeper. Everything is moving ahead, whether we wish this or not. Men come in three categories: Some are in the forefront and expend all their efforts to advance science, culture, and humanity; these are men of progress. Others, and they are in a majority, walk by the side of progress; they neither hinder nor help. Finally there are individuals who lag behind and try to stop progress; these are conservatives, men who are cowards and bereft of imagination.

Four Men of Science

Those who walk in the vanguard have the hardest lot. They blaze new trails for progress; fate assails them with all manner of trials. Such a man was Paul Langevin, and his life was full of heavy ordeals. The question arises, why do such people as he choose such a path? What compels them to march in the forefront when it is so much more pleasant and peaceful to walk on the sidelines, if not to lag behind completely? I think there are two reasons for this. A wise man cannot help but be for progress. To act in the cause of progress, to comprehend things that are new, and to understand the goals of such new things—all this only a wise person can do, a man who is endowed with boldness and imagination. But this is not enough. When wisdom is combined with the proper temperament, a man becomes really progressive. Paul Langevin was such a man. In life most frequently we observe that only in his youth is a man's temperament at its most tempestuous, and this is what makes the man progressive. As he ages, a man wants to live in peace and quiet. This is why young people, particularly in their student years, are mankind's most progressive part. But no such thing happened in Langevin's life. He was a fighter for progress till his life's end. The older he grew the more zealously did he fight in the cause of progress. It was this unusual ingredient in him that always impressed me and evoked my profound sympathy and respect.

And now I want to give you a brief review of his scientific activity from this standpoint of Langevin as a man of progress.

His first researches were in magnetism, and he did these in 1907. In this work he was the first to apply statistical mechanics, at that time developed and generalized by Ludwig Boltzmann,[3] to the laws of para- and diamagnetism, which had shortly before then been discovered by Pierre Curie, Langevin's teacher and friend.

Now we take this for granted, but if we reconstruct the state of physics of that period, we will see that in their essence these contributions meant an extraordinary progress. During those years Boltzmann's ideas were being accepted only with great difficulty. Boltzmann committed suicide in 1906 for no other reason than that the basic, bold idea which he had used as the premise of his work in the kinetic theory of matter— the connection of entropy with the probability of bringing about molecular states—was neither understood nor recognized. The period's leading scientists, among them Ostwald,[4] did not at all wish to recognize the atomistic theory, and a storm raged around Boltzmann's work. But Langevin regarded his own initial researches in magnetism precisely from the standpoint of these new views held by Boltzmann.

A little later or almost at the same time Einstein's work on the theory of relativity appeared. It was published in 1905. Already fifty years have passed since then, and now only the most die-hard conservatives object to the basic ideas of the theory of relativity. But when it first appeared, there was of course a stream of objections, and the bitterest of these were naturally against that law which for the first time was expressed with complete clarity and with such ample quantity of data—the law of the equality of mass to energy. This equality is defined by the law, according to which a mass of matter, multiplied by the square of the speed of light, may be transformed into an equal quantity of energy. A number of scientists saw in this a violation of the law of preservation of energy and of the law of preservation of matter, both of which were then the fundamentals of physics; it was this that brought a storm of objections.

Langevin was among the very first in France to propagandize Einstein's ideas. Almost simultaneously with Einstein's discovery of his law, Langevin published his work wherein he pointed out that the possibility of the difference between the deviation of whole numbers of masses in the periodic system of elements from the whole numbers of the multiples of hydrogen was connected with the fact that in complex atoms there appears an excess of energy that increases their atomic weight. We now know that this was a correct prediction, one that could be made only by a great scientist, and it was later confirmed in experiments repeatedly. Nowadays these views have a precise theoretical foundation. This once more shows the

143

way Langevin accepted new ideas in science and the way he actually used them. Of course we now have the atomic bomb, which has demonstrated to all mankind the enormous force of the explosion caused by the transformation of matter into energy. Simple calculations show that in the process of such a transformation in the atomic bomb just one gram of matter becomes energy, and in the hydrogen bomb no more than a kilogram is enough. Einstein, Langevin, and other leading physicists had repeatedly said that such an enormous result was possible, yet there were many who did not believe this. It is difficult to have a more convincing demonstration of the Einstein law than came in the bomb explosions at Hiroshima and Nagasaki. And yet, despite this, we at our editorial office of *Zhurnal eksperimental'noi i teoreticheskoi fiziki* even to this day [1957] receive articles in which attempts are made to refute the theory of relativity. These days such articles are not even given any consideration whatever, for they are clearly antiscience. Such is the second example of how, fifty years ago, Langevin was already taking a leading and right road in physics.

The third case illustrating his progressiveness in modern physics was observed by me personally. I came to see Langevin in Paris in 1924. He was then a professor at the Collège de France. He greeted me with these words: "My student de Broglie has carried out a remarkable piece of work, and I want him to tell you about it." He called de Broglie and, in my presence, asked him to tell me of his latest work on the wave nature of electrons. Since that time this work has become classic. I saw then how absorbed Langevin was in this work. It is entirely possible that but for Langevin's support de Broglie would not have approached his remarkable idea with the boldness needed to develop and carry it out.

The following example will show the considerable skepticism with which this idea was then greeted. On returning from Paris, I spoke to the Cambridge theoreticians about de Broglie's work. Paul Dirac [5] was as yet a student then; he was in my class on magnetism, usually sitting in the first row. I did not foresee that in time he would be an outstanding scientist who would find for de Broglie's idea a most general mathematical expression. Fowler was then the main theoretician at Cambridge. Neither he nor his associates wished to recognize de Broglie's views as something serious. And when I offered to report on this subject at a seminar, they said to me: "We won't waste time on this." But already a year or two later, when Schroedinger [6] did his work wherein he generalized de Broglie's ideas mathematically, and when there appeared Schroedinger's equation, now regarded as classic, where he showed that what de Broglie had accomplished was nothing else but establish a proper significance of functions in certain equations, the fundamental importance of de Broglie's work became clear to everybody in the field.

The story of Schroedinger's creation of his equations is most instructive. Debye,[7] with whom Schroedinger was then working, told me this story. Having read de Broglie's work, Debye suggested that Schroedinger report about it at a seminar. Shroedinger said something like, "I don't want to talk about such nonsense." But Debye, in his capacity as senior leader of the seminar, insisted. Schroedinger had to agree. He decided to present de Broglie's ideas in a mathematical way that would be better understood at the seminar. He thus succeeded in creating the equations which now bear his name and which brought him fame among the scientists of the entire world.

Debye related that when Schroedinger was delivering his seminar report, he himself was unaware of the magnitude of his discovery. Right then and there, at the seminar, Debye said to him: "You have done a remarkable job." But Schroedinger merely thought that he had found a convenient way of telling these physicists just what it was that de Broglie had done. And all this happened two years after the appearance of de Broglie's publication. Yet Langevin from the very beginning, ahead of all the others, had understood that a new science of physics was to come from de Broglie's ideas. This example once more shows Langevin's wonderful sense of what was progress. In my conversations with Langevin I was always struck by his broad vision of what was happening in science. His ability to see ahead was positively awe-inspiring.

In the sphere of public affairs Langevin stood for progress as much as he did in physics. He often said proudly: "I was born at Montmartre." This was then known as the most proletarian part of Paris. Langevin's grandfather was a simple locksmith, and his father a land surveyor. Langevin himself was born in 1872 in poverty. He went through a city school, and then, with the aid of scholarships, he gained his higher education. He was a truly talented man, and he was of course a brilliant student. Later he became a pupil of Pierre Curie, who sent him to the Cavendish Laboratory, where Langevin worked in the same room as Rutherford. Already then Cambridge was a center of physics study. The chief professor at the Cavendish Laboratory was J. J. Thomson, whose fame was in his discovery of the electron. The research done by him on the passage of electricity through gas was as much in the forefront of science then as nuclear physics has become in recent times.

At Cambridge, Langevin did his first experimental work; it was there that his scientific career began. Following this, for many years, Langevin enjoyed a close friendship with British scientists, particularly with Rutherford. A man of charm, Langevin attracted to himself persons of practically any class; he had friends everywhere. Returning to Paris, Langevin began to work at the Collège de France, where in time he succeeded to Pierre Curie's chair. His very first works on magnetism made him one of the foremost physicists of France.

He began his political activity also quite early, while still a student. Its start was connected with the notorious Dreyfus Affair, this shameful episode contrived by a group of anti-Semites who may be considered as predecessors of Fascists. You will recall that Emile Zola wrote his famous "J'accuse" in defense of Dreyfus.

When Zola was persecuted, Langevin rose in his defense. This was his first public appearance as a civic leader. Later, in his frequent reminiscences of this activity on his part, he would say: "Yes, those were the good times when—imagine!—the entire planet could become interested in one man's fate." Following this he was politically active on many other occasions.

Thus in 1920 in Paris, at a meeting in Wagram Hall, he delivered a passionate speech in defense of the sailors of the [French] Black Sea fleet who had refused to fight against the young Soviet republic. With the same sensitivity that he displayed in science, Langevin envisaged the progressive significance of our [Soviet] social revolution and at once, openly, came out in its support.

The same year, during a transport strike in Paris, he, a university professor, protested against the use of students as strike-breakers.

Together with Romain Rolland and Henri Barbusse he was unflinchingly active against Fascism.

During the Leipzig trial he came out in Dimitrov's [8] defense. He was one of the most active defenders of Ernst Thaelmann.[9] He was one of the organizers of the League of Human Rights and served as its president. On numerous occasions he spoke up for the Spanish republic.

In this recital we repeatedly read "spoke up," "came out for," "defended." Behind these words were his great civic activity and tremendous organizational efforts.

Langevin came out with a passionate denunciation of the Munich Pact, and against the arrest of twenty-seven [French] Communist deputies at the war's start.

When the war broke out, I was given the opportunity to offer to Langevin refuge in the Soviet Union for the duration of the conflict, and so wrote to him. Knowing the Fascists' hatred for him, I feared for his survival if he remained in France. It was of course imperative to give him a chance to leave for a country where he would be safe and where he could continue to be active on behalf of France. In his answering letter he wrote that he would come to the Soviet Union with pleasure, but right now he must finish one job, namely: an anti-Semitic movement had been started at the University of Paris, and Langevin headed the fight against it; so long as this movement remained undefeated, he felt he had no right to leave Paris.

When Langevin finally decided that he could leave Paris, it was already too late: Hitler's government refused to let him pass through Germany. Then Paris was taken by the German troops. Langevin was at once arrested. He was imprisoned for two months and afterward sent to a small town where he became a teacher of physics at a girls' high school. He held this job through the first half of the war.

Langevin's family, all of them, were in the Resistance. Langevin's daughter was arrested; she was sent to the concentration camp at Auschwitz, where she nevertheless survived. Her husband, Solomon, a well-known Communist, was executed by the Germans. Langevin had to leave France. This was not easy, for he was nearly seventy. He fled across the mountains to Switzerland. For this, an automobile accident was faked; he was bandaged and carried in men's arms over the mountains. He stayed in Switzerland the entire second half of the war, and from there he participated in the liberation movement as much as his strength permitted. On learning of the execution of his son-in-law Solomon, he wrote a letter to Duclos [10] asking to be enrolled in the Communist Party as a replacement for Solomon. And thus, from 1942 to the day of his death, on December 19, 1946, he was one of the most active members of the Communist Party.

I think that this brief recital of facts affords a clear enough picture of Langevin's civic and political activity. This shows that there was not in Europe, particularly in France, a single event in the cause of progress without Langevin's active participation. In addition, there was his liveliest participation in the problems of education. I remember how, during a visit in Paris, I told Langevin that I had to go to Strasbourg to deliver a lecture at the university. Langevin said: "Very well, let's travel together. I am also about to go to Strasbourg; I am to lecture there on the teaching of the French language in Alsace." I attended his lecture, just as he came to mine, and heard how interestingly he handled the question of French language instruction in Alsace. This was not an easy task, insofar as a complex political problem was connected with it, the sympathies of the population being divided between France and Germany, and Langevin had to use considerable tact in what he said. Listening to him, I realized with what consummate skill he had built his speech.

Such is the sum of his activity.

A man who stood for progress so well in science and in society could not fail but attract followers, particularly among young people.

Langevin was twenty years my senior, but, despite this difference in our ages, it was most easy to be with him. He was an exceptionally charming man and was loved by the masses. Even some of those who held political views opposite to his were friendly to him. His gentleness, his extraordinarily good heart, and his responsiveness disarmed and conquered everyone. With any person, be it prime minister or student, he used the very same language, and both felt completely at ease with him.

As an example of the regard felt for him by people of all stations, let me cite the telegram sent to the Paris Academy by Einstein upon the news of Langevin's death. This is a very short telegram, and I have selected it not because it was written by Einstein, but because in my opinion it expresses extremely well and briefly just who Langevin really was.

> The news of Langevin's death shocked me more than many other disappointments and tragedies which have happened in these years. How few people there are in one generation uniting in themselves a clear understanding of the essence of things with a sharp feeling of truly humane demands and an ability to act energetically! When such a man leaves us we feel the emptiness which seems unbearable for those who remain!

In conclusion I want to mention one small feature of his character which lends yet more charm and humanity to his personality. Langevin had one weakness: he loved wine. He loved it not in any vulgar sense. He loved the wine's aroma; he loved wine as a professional winetaster would. He used to say: "One does not drink wine—one talks of it!" He would take a glass of wine, he would hold it in his hand, he would inhale its aroma—and say this was a Burgundy of such and such a year and brand, of such and such a crop of grapes, distinguished by such and such qualities. He could declaim a whole poem about this glass of wine. He was proud of his knowledge of wines. This was, as the English say, his hobby.

Once in Zurich, for the duration of a conference, I shared a restaurant table with him. At each meal he would most carefully choose the rarest wine and right then and there would lecture to me on the subject of this wine. His knowledge of wines was not at all amateurish. French wine makers would invite him to their vineyards after a harvest of grapes to hear his appraisal as to what kind of wine might come in a few years from these grapes. He would go on such trips, very proud that those Burgundy wine makers valued his opinion. But above all he was proud of the fact that once, while winetasting in the Var River valley in the south of France, he "discovered" a new and excellent wine. The result was that, because of his appraisal, a high-quality wine was created out of some plebeian red wine.

He sincerely rejoiced and was bursting with pride that it was he who had discovered this high-level wine. With great passion he spoke of the wine of this new sort discovered by him in the Var valley, and not of the theory of magnetism, which was his real greatest triumph.

Such is a short account of the activity and the image of this outstanding man of progress. I count it as great rare luck for me that I happened to have known and loved this remarkable man, to have been in his company.

II

MISCELLANEOUS
ESSAYS
AND SPEECHES

1

Unity of Science and Technology

[*Based on an article in the Moscow* Pravda *of June 17, 1941*]

The life of a socialist state is built and develops on scientific foundations. Therefore from the very first days of its existence the Soviet regime has been showing great attention to and concern for science. The result is that we now have a science which solves problems that are most up-to-date and difficult. We also have an industry which produces extremely fine and complex mechanisms. But the connection between our science and technology is as yet weak, and this hampers us in our full utilization of the entire rich reserve of our country's creative forces.

Science and technology can help each other only when there is a lively and healthy union between them. Science must open before technology new opportunities, and technology should seize these boldly, without being urged to do so. As technology grows, not only is science in turn enriched by new technical possibilities, but also its themes are broadened and become better directed to better aims.

153

Nowhere is there such fertile ground for the widest possible application of science as in the Soviet Union. We therefore can explain the as yet weak union of our science and technology only by the fact that the most effective organizational forms of such a connection are still not found by us. Doubtless, given our level of science and technology, and considering the deficiencies which have not as yet been eliminated, we could reach far greater achievements of creative technology. I do not think that this delay can be explained solely by such evident and gradually disappearing deficiencies as a certain clutter of our creative personnel by noncreative men, bureaucratic tendencies, lack of order in our supplies, and the like. It seems to me that we suffer also from more significant deficiencies in organization, which are not discussed enough.

A strategy and a tactical approach all their own are needed in the struggle to master nature successfully. Here, as in any battle, the most important task is that of a correct distribution of forces along the front and a clear directive to the soldiers.

The army of science must be inspired by problems set before it. It must feel the importance of the victories expected of it on the sectors assigned to it. Also, it is necessary to form fighting units skillfully and to furnish them with responsible commanders. Life has demonstrated that all kinds of pressures on creative toilers of science and technology are effective only when a healthy public opinion supports such pressures. This opinion is shaped at scientific sessions and by the press. And this most important organizational opportunity is being utilized by us as yet insufficiently.

As an example let us take the general sessions of the Academy of Sciences. They are well attended. They are marked by interesting reports on their agenda. But more frequently these are professorial lectures meant to round out listeners' educations; they are not scientific discussions. Hardly any debates occur. We have no tradition of evaluating publicly this or that scientific or technical problem and the researches connected with such problems. There is not even a desire to start a debate.

Yet, debates cannot arise spontaneously; they must be cultivated. For this, it is necessary to choose most important and acute questions well in advance, and simultaneously to select and prepare opponents. The chairman should direct the debate; he ought to state the controversial theses and see to it that the participants do not stray from the basic problems. If, by its very nature, the given scientific report arouses no discussion—if, let us say, it is simply a report about a scientific discovery—even then the meeting should hear the opinion of leading experts in the field, so that a correct public appraisal is made. There is no reason whatever to schedule public reports if they are not accompanied by debates and discussions. It would be simpler and cheaper to print them without reading them aloud at public sessions.

It often seems to me as if in our scientific milieu we are afraid of debates and definite appraisals. This is so perhaps because we still fear to hurt one another's false pride, based on the mistaken notion that a good scientist cannot err, since an "error" will discredit him. We seem to forget that "only he does not err who does nothing." After all, any scientific truth of today may be amplified or altered tomorrow, for we are in a state of ceaseless approach to the knowledge of the true nature of things. Only if we overcome one mistake after another, in the process revealing contradictions, do we gain a yet closer solution of the problem at hand. Errors are not yet a pseudo science. A pseudo science refuses to recognize mistakes. This is why a pseudo science is a brake on healthy scientific development.

We must note that often our press also shies away from a discussion of controversial problems of science and technology.

The absence of a healthy public opinion concerning a number of problems not only causes the possibility of emergence in our country of harmful or worthless work in science, but also hampers the concentration of our best forces around central problems.

The lack of discussions does not at all become our general premises, which are that every scientific and technical achievement is the property of the entire nation, and that people want not only to understand it but also to appraise it. And a just public appraisal inspires the scientific worker and helps create that enthusiasm which is so vital in creative work. Each and every scientific and technical problem of significance has a public value in our country. It should therefore be discussed, and there must be a verdict regarding it.

It seems to me that the organization of the army of creative workers in our industry is even less developed than in the realm of science. If our scientists are nonetheless united in a certain collective organization, the creative workers of our technology are so scattered throughout the enormous expanse of our industry that it is very difficult to concentrate them into a battering ram when this is needed.

Again I shall speak not of those rather petty battles that result in a series of technical improvements, such as the choice of materials that are more proper than others, or the rationalization of various processes of production, or economizing in the use of the working force, the rise of the product's quality, and so on. Such a growth of technology, even though often it is maintained in a "guerrilla" manner by separate enthusiasts, has great significance and generally is done by us rather well. The most remarkable point about it, of course, is that in our country this growth involves—as nowhere else—the broadest masses of technical toilers, from workers to engineers. But I have in mind battles that are more important, that are being carried on by large subdivisions of such talent, and that will result in providing this country with unprecedented opportunities.

In such large battles, even if we spend a great deal of labor and other means, if we mobilize the best creative team possible of scientists and engineers who would work persistently and with enthusiasm, still it is impossible to guarantee victory over nature beforehand. But if a battle is won, this means a new phase in the development of industry. Achievements of this category will enable us to overtake everybody. It is subject to no doubt that a socialist way should be a better organizer of such great victories in technology. Under no circumstances can capitalism mobilize men and means so broadly for such a battle.

To utilize this exceptional opportunity, again we must learn to organize rapidly a veritable army of our best creative workers in all the leading areas of technology and to coordinate their work with that of our scientists.

As I observe it, the most significant organizational deficiency is in the fact that we do not attach proper importance to problems connected with putting new gains of technology into practice, for usually we do not consider such gains as truly creative. At local research institutes and in plants' laboratories good conditions have been established for creative work. And at the same time, the utilization of new ideas—this very last link in the chain—is usually done by the rank-and-file personnel with no more exertion than that expended in the carrying-out of their current production tasks. But just as a person is never shaped into a good citizen suddenly but has to be cultivated to that stage in a prolonged effort, so a new idea responsible for certain machines or processes comes forth only as these machines or processes grow and develop. A successful "upbringing" of new ideas should be entrusted not to a rank-and-file engineer, foreman, or worker but to a carefully selected and highly skilled creative collective.

I came across this absence, in our production, of organized cadres of creative technical workers of this type when I had to build installations blueprinted by us to obtain liquid air and oxygen. These installations, operating on new principles of liquefying and separating, were tried out successfully in a laboratory only. Now industry had the assignment to construct, from this installation, a machine that could be reliably used in actual production.

Our greatest difficulties were in the organization of groundwork for such a practical transfer from the laboratory to the plant, also in finding the necessary cadres of engineers, technicians, designers, skilled workers, and others capable of mastering such machines creatively. Of course, there are enough of such persons in our industry, but they are little known as such —they are not recognized readily enough. They are scattered, they are not indexed, they do all kinds of other work. You have to search for them as if feeling your way in the dark. And when you do find them, it is not easy to obtain them for your plant. Our industrial officials, not yet comprehending all the importance of achieving new opportunities in technology, frequently oppose the recruitment of these excellent men; they are against establishing special conditions necessary to carry out such special assignments.

The importance of laying healthy groundwork for the introduction of new achievements of technology may be seen from what a certain foreign firm did when it was compelled by circumstances to organize an experimental plant intended essentially to try out new types of machines. This is the Brown-Boveri plant in Switzerland.[1] It was built in the city of Baden, not too far distant from the University of Zurich. Using Dr. Stodola [2] and other prominent professors as consultants, the plant produced very good electrical machines and turbines. But as the surrounding countries began to erect their customs barriers, the concern was forced to build independent plants in Canada, Germany, France, and other countries. At that, the technical creation of new machines was concentrated in Baden, where the firm gathered its best personnel. It was perhaps thus that in Baden there emerged one of the world's best experimental plants.

Of course, we are not so much interested in the causes that led to its emergence as in the extent of success that can be reached by a plant whose basic aim is to create and master nothing but new types of machines. As an example of its triumph let me point out that this plant produced the world's very first successfully functioning gas turbine. In this example we can see the strength that emerges when in one place there are concentrated the best possible creative forces of science and technology, directed to solve definite tasks and possessing also a special base from which to put their achievements into practice.

Unity of Science and Technology

Therefore I think it is timely to pose the question of uniting, in each field of our industry, well-selected collectives of creative workers of all types. Depending on the scale of production, it is imperative for this organization to include separate shops of plants, and in a large field it will have to embrace even independent plants with their specially chosen cadres. In this way we will establish considerably better conditions for the introduction into our industry of entirely new directions of technology. Given a thoughtful and flexible guidance, such collectives will doubtless fling doors wide open into technology for all of our science, and this will lead to the introduction of the boldest and most progressive ideas possible. Then it will be much easier to establish liaison between the scientific and technical collectives of creative personnel. And this will prove a big step forward, narrowing yet more the currently wide separation between theory and life. After all, this separation owes its existence mainly to certain temporary organizational gaps. But actually, as we see with an ever-sharpening clarity, it is increasingly difficult to discover just where science ends and precisely at what point its direct connection with life begins.[3]

2

The Institute of Problems of Physics

[From a report made at the meeting of the Presidium of the Soviet Academy of Sciences on May 18, 1943]

When I returned to work in the Soviet Union, I was very much interested in the problem of the organization of science in general, and of scientific research at my Institute in particular. I was well aware of the way science and scientific research were organized abroad. For a number of years I had served as director of an institute at Cambridge, that center of British scientific thought. On the basis of that experience I felt that the organizational forms of scientific work customary in the West were not entirely suitable to the Soviet Union. I thought that we had to seek different organizational forms for scientific research in our Institute and, yet more, in the organization of all our science.

This is so mainly because in our socialist country a special place is set aside for science. Of course, in other lands, too, it is well known and commonly assumed that science plays an important role in the development of a given country's culture and technology. But in our country science is recognized as one of the significant and basic pillars of the cultural development. Science in our country is held to be a leading force in the development of our technology and national economy. Therefore the organization of science in our country must have a more sharply defined aim than we witness in capitalistic countries, where such an organization is rather of a haphazard, spontaneous nature. In the Soviet Union the bond between science and life must be closer and fuller. And for us, who work at the Soviet Academy of Sciences, problems of the organization of science are especially important.

As I proceed to tell you about the organization of scientific research in our Institute, I will first of all endeavor to provide a picture of those general principles of organization of science which we used as our premise, and then I will describe precisely what we have succeeded in accomplishing.

But let me utter a word of caution, namely: I will speak, essentially, of the Institute's organization in peacetime. As to how the Institute has changed its personality for the period of war, how we have adapted it to the needs of wartime—this will be covered in a few words at the end of my report. The wartime phase of our Institute should of course be regarded as temporary only. Of more lasting interest is the Institute's structure as it existed before this war. The healthier this structure the more easily it can be adapted for the fighting times, no matter when these come.

I also wish to remind you that our Institute is young. It has been in existence only seven or eight years. Although at the time of my arrival here I was already a more or less recognized scientist, I found it difficult to create an institute while having neither a school nor a staff of my own. Therefore the Institute grew much more slowly than would have been the case had it branched originally off some other institute, and had it continued to develop and grow independently from such a beginning. Additional difficulties in the recruitment of our personnel were caused by the singularities of our work, which dealt in strong magnetic fields and low temperatures—a field of scientific research then as yet little developed in the Soviet Union. The first years were spent by us in the formation and training of the basic scientific personnel and servicing staff of the Institute. Only after the working nucleus was gathered could the Institute begin its normal growth and expansion.

From the very start I put this question before myself: what should the tasks of an institute of the Academy of Sciences be? In asking this question, I had in mind of course an institute of physics or generally an institute devoted to researches in the realm of the natural sciences. The tasks and the organization of an institute working in other fields of knowledge will certainly be different. Therefore I warn you beforehand against making too sweeping a generalization of the theses which I will develop in this report.

Let me further stress that the subject at hand is the organization of an institute of no other kind than that belonging to the Academy of Sciences. What is the Academy of Sciences? This is the general staff of Soviet science. In my opinion the Academy is meant to guide and supply with ideas all of our science from top to bottom—to guide it along a healthy channel.

Each and every institute of the Academy should pursue the very same policy, that is, it should strive to exert a leader's influence on science in the field of its work, to see to it that science in this field is carried on to the most advanced levels possible.

Therefore the very first task that an institute of the Academy should set before itself is to be occupied with large issues of science. Science of large issues is the science that studies fundamental phenomena indispensable for the deepest possible comprehension of nature. The task of such science is to provide the knowledge necessary for the transformation of nature in such a way that nature would serve man in his cultural development. Therefore it is most essential to choose correctly the basic themes of the institute, to select the fields for its work's direction. This direction of the institute must be consonant with that direction in the development of science which at the moment is most promising, which in a given state of science, and taking into account the possible methods, can move ahead most swiftly and fruitfully.

I think that in the field of physics there now exist three such basic directions: research in the area of low temperatures; research in the area of the atomic nucleus; and, finally, research in the area of solids. I cannot now stop to explain the reasons why I consider these directions most important, and perhaps a number of my fellow physicists will not agree with me. Our Institute is presently studying the phenomena occurring at low temperatures, near the absolute zero. Let me note that in recent years this direction has been one of fastest developing in physics, and it is possible to expect within it many new and fundamental discoveries.

A small number of leading personnel carry out scientific research in our Institute. This makes the Institute's work flow toward certain definite aims; it concentrates its research around a small number of important subjects. Nothing is as dangerous for an institute's scientific research as cluttering it up with petty themes, distracting the staff from basic themes and efforts. The fundamental list of our Institute's themes is drawn up by a small number of its scientific personnel, by three or four scientists, and the result is a definite aim for our research.

After the choice of the general direction of an institute's work is made, the next important question to solve is the recruitment of its scientific staff. Meaningful successes can be achieved in higher science by that man only who is gifted with a deep creativeness and who treats his work just as creatively. There are not many such persons in science, and, at that, there cannot be many of them, just as a nation cannot possess many truly outstanding writers, composers, and artists. But when we do happen to have these talented people, we must surround them with such care that their scientific strength can be utilized for the development of our higher science in the fullest and most proper manner possible. Therefore the core of an institute can surely be formed only out of a small number of very thoroughly selected scientific workers.

This core should devote itself to scientific work completely. An institute should be so organized, and the conditions for work in it should be created in such a way, that its scientific workers would spend in the laboratory and be busy with science not less than eighty per cent of their time, while their social and other functions would occupy not more than twenty per cent of their time. Only under such conditions can we achieve a state of affairs wherein the scientific personnel will stay in the laboratory and work completely on their own. It is only when you yourself work in the laboratory, and with your own hands perform the experiments, be it often thought the most routine part of these experiments, that you can accomplish real results in science. You cannot do good work with other people's hands. A man who devotes only a few minutes now and then to the job of guiding scientific research cannot be a first-rank scientist. At any rate I have never seen, and have never heard about, a prominent scientist with such work habits. I am confident that the moment even the greatest scientist stops his own work in the laboratory, he not only ceases his growth, but is no longer a scientist. These principles are very important, but they are valid for peacetime only, because during a war we have to behave and act differently.

It is particularly important for scientists who are just beginning their careers to accept these principles. This is why I try to channel their research into a rather strict organizational framework. For instance, a scientific worker must not tackle several themes at once, especially if he is at the very start of his path. As a scientific worker grows in stature, as he gains prominence, he may perhaps be able—as a rare exception—to press on with two or three research themes simultaneously, but one theme is the rule at the beginning.

Next in our list of organizational methods, important for the achievement of success in research, is the rule that a scientific worker should toil in his laboratory a limited number of hours.

The Institute of Problems of Physics

To become "drunk" with your work is harmful. Such a work method exhausts you and lowers your creative strength. The rule in our Institute, for instance, is that at six in the evening all work in the laboratory stops. The staff member must go home—to think about his work, to read, to study, and to rest.[1] Only in exceptional cases, and if permitted by the assistant director, can he work until eight in the evening. Night work is allowed only by leave of the director himself; it may be justified by technical requirements caused by the specific conditions of the given experiment. Such is the working regime for our Institute's scientific staff.

An institute, even when by the quality of its scientific force and the quality of its production it can become the center of a higher science, may nonetheless develop as a self-isolated, withdrawn unit and not satisfy the demands originally set.

How can, then, an institute exert its influence on the growth of the nation's high-level science? How can it connect itself with other centers of the nation's scientific thought? There are several ways for this. Let us mention the chief among them.

First of all, it should utilize those advantages which it enjoys in its status as an institute of the Academy of Sciences. These advantages include abundant, modern technical equipment, also a well-selected staff, thanks to which it is feasible to carry out certain scientific activities impossible of accomplishment at other institutes. At our Institute, for instance, the presence of a special installation to obtain large quantities of liquid helium opens exceptional opportunities to experiment in the field of low temperatures, opportunities lacking in other places. And so, taking advantage of this, our Institute allows staff members of other institutes to come as working visitors—to do at our Institute work in the area of low temperatures which cannot be done in any other place. These researches, however, are not ordinarily of first importance; they are at times outside the basic themes of our Institute.

Such visits from other institutes are usually organized in the following fashion. The colleague who wants to work in our Institute is invited to make a report at our scientific session or seminar explaining the experiment he intends to conduct in our laboratory. His project is discussed. If the proposal appears to have a solidly grounded scientific interest, and the applicant is sufficiently qualified, he is given this opportunity to conduct his experiment. In order not to hamper our Institute's basic researches, we limit the number of such outside projects. Usually there are no more than two or three of them at a time.

Of those desiring to research in our Institute there have so far been more than we can accommodate. This is a good indicator of the fact that the Institute is indeed in the forefront of science, for otherwise the outside scientific establishments would not be so interested in our work and would not wish for contacts with us.

The constant presence at our Institute of personnel from other scientific establishments has enabled us to effect one of the ways of lively liaison with the outside scientific world. On completing their work and leaving our Institute, such scientific guests not only profit from the experience gained in the process of their research, but also acquaint other institutes with our work, and so our work penetrates farther and yet farther into the nation's other scientific organizations. It is thus through these guests that a lively contact with other institutes is established, and we in our turn become aware of just what these other institutes are doing. This is the strongest contact there is. Its utilization is a good method of influencing further development of our country's science.

It is imperative to organize the same kind of live contacts also with foreign scientists. In the first years of our Institute's existence we were visited by scientists from abroad. But in recent years the political situation has become so complicated that, although there are indeed those who wish to come, the general contact with foreign countries has been disturbed, so that we can now talk about our contact with foreign scientists in terms of the future only. But such contact should be viewed as a normal and healthy condition of the work of any academic institute, since all science in the world constitutes one unbroken entity. If an academic institute wishes to occupy a leading place, one mark of such an actual achievement is when those desirous to work in it are not alone citizens of the given country but scientists of other countries as well. This would be proof enough that the institute in question indeed conducts scientific research of major importance and high quality.

Secondly, there is one more field of influence exerted upon our culture and our science by high-level academic institutes. This is the field of scientific-cadres training.

An institute itself should train its own future personnel, and this must be done by educating the young ones with great care, and gradually. Therefore we should in all ways welcome and support the system of graduate studies as it has grown up in the Soviet Union. But there are certain difficulties in this area, and I want to discuss them.

One such difficulty is in the choice of graduate students. The crux of the matter lies in the unsatisfactory liaison prevailing in a number of cases between our scientific establishments on the one hand and our colleges and universities on the other. This, I think, is a serious deficiency in our organization. The best, the most prominent, of our scientists have gone into the institutions of scientific research. The direction of colleges and universities has remained mainly in the hands of the professional pedagogues, and research work is not the chief part of their activity. Most of our professors, let me say this bluntly, cannot be regarded as our country's leading scientists. What they demand of students, their system of educating our youth, is usually not at all aimed at finding and encouraging such young men and women as are creatively strong. Therefore, in our schools of higher learning, the creative beginnings of our young usually are developed poorly.

While attending examinations of graduate students, I have frequently noted that such professors give the highest marks not to the student who has the best understanding but to the student who knows most. Yet, science needs people who, first of all, understand. Therefore, by their showing at examinations, it is extremely difficult to select students fit for graduate studies. To choose promising graduates correctly, it is necessary to observe them during a certain period of time when they are occupied with work of the kind that gives them a chance to demonstrate their creative predilections, their ability to think on their own.

It seems to me that this gap between our colleges and universities on the one hand and our scientific institutes on the other is precisely the cause of the phenomenon that the selection of young scientific cadres is far less fruitful now than it was in my time, when main scientific work was conducted at our teaching institutes and other such schools and not at scientific institutes. I recall the period when Academician A. F. Ioffe [2] was the chief professor of physics at the Polytechnic Institute in Leningrad. It was not accidental, I believe, that precisely then a number of beginning scientists of promising talents (by now four of them already members of the Academy) gravitated into Ioffe's group of scientific workers. At the present time, too, our schools of higher learning doubtless contain many promising and talented young men and women, but the sieve which we use as we try to screen these people for scientific work has such holes that a number of talented students slip by and do not go into scientific institutes. If we wish to start selection of the most talented scientists, we must seriously ponder the question of just how to find a form of better liaison between our scientific institutes and our schools, so as to discover and bring up the young of most creative talents.

This is why we have begun to search for new ways of selecting graduate students from among those finishing their undergraduate years. A certain way of choosing, which we introduced for our Institute, began to develop only during the last two or three years before the war, and it is as yet difficult to say what results it will bring. And this is the method. Taking advantage of the fact that for experiments conducted at low temperatures we possess liquid helium in greater quantities than those held by all the refrigerating laboratories of the world put together, we had the opportunity of organizing at the Institute a practicum, through which every student of the department of physics of the Moscow University passes. Of course, such a practicum was at first organized for the best students only, but in the last two years all the department of physics students without an exception passed through this practicum, and, at that, each student carried out two or three laboratory experiments with liquid helium. From the standpoint of cryogen [3] institutes this is a big luxury, since in the Leyden laboratory, for instance, and in other laboratories, work with liquid helium is to this day considered to be hardly accessible, even for scientists. But with us, each and every student of the Moscow University has had the opportunity to conduct research on, say, the qualities of superconductors, magnetic phenomena at temperatures close to the absolute zero, and so on. Naturally, the University welcomed such an opportunity and readily sent its students to us. In the process of the work of the practicum the following system was established: the top students, those with the best showing in the work of the practicum, were singled out, and, in case they wished this, they could do more than the three stipulated pieces of research. At that, the scientific staff who ran the practicum talked to them and then sent the best ones to talk to me. In this way we had the opportunity to find the most capable young men and women, to get together with them closely beginning with their third or fourth University year, and to keep track of them. Further, the best of these were invited by us to become "practicians" at the Institute. In this capacity, even before graduation, they participated in our researches as junior laboratory workers, helped our scientific staff in the latter's experiments, took notes, organized the simpler of our experiments, and so forth.

From these "practician" cadres our selection of young men and women for graduate studies was done, not alone on the basis of their performance on their university examinations but also on the basis of their performance while working at our Institute. Of course, such a screening of young scientists allows us to involve a wider circle of young ones and to remove the element of the accidental. The war interrupted our experiment. But had we gone on with it, there would have been this development: having finished their graduate studies, having gained their degrees as candidates in the sciences, these young scientists would have gone into other scientific establishments and would have disseminated the scientific experience of our Institute. We could have further expected that one out of every ten or fifteen such men completing their graduate studies would prove so talented as to remain at our Institute on the main staff of our creative scientists. And so our Institute would have continued to grow.

Such a method of observing the young students from their University years on, such a thorough and ceaseless checking of their abilities, in my opinion constitutes thus far the only right way of selecting young scientific cadres. We must not spare our strength when we do this work of screening, and not only because these young scientific cadres are our future. They are also our present. As you grow older, only your young students can save you from a premature hardening of the brain. Each student working in his field is also a teacher. Who else teaches the teacher but his own pupils? Thanks to his experience, the teacher guides the work's direction, but in the final analysis the pupils teach the teacher—they deepen his knowledge and broaden his horizon. Without his disciples a scientist usually perishes very quickly as a creative unit; he ceases his forward movement. Never will I forget the words of my great teacher Rutherford. "Kapitsa," he used to say, "you know that only thanks to my students do I keep on feeling young." And as I myself approach my old age, I feel that being with young people must be that *modus vivendi* which safeguards you from fading and which guarantees a preservation of alertness in you, of your interest in everything new and front-rank in science. After all, conservatism in science is for a scientist worse than premature death; this is a brake on the development of science.

Thirdly, let us discuss one more important variety of contact between an institute's scientific work and the outside world. This type of contact, it seems to me, is unjustly ignored not only in scientific institutes, but also at the Academy of Sciences as a whole. This is the problem of propagandizing science.

We talk a lot about the popularization of science, meaning by this making it popular for the broad masses, but we are not accustomed to the thought that, besides such a popularization, there exists also the propaganda of science.[4] Every major achievement of science, each step forward in science, is susceptible to its popularization—and popularization, of course, is not a scientist's obligation. But a scientist is obliged to propagandize it, that is, to demonstrate to his fellow scientists its significance, to explain that role in science which this accomplishment is destined to play, to point out what influence it may exert on the development of scientific thought, on our philosophical views, on our technology, and so forth. The propaganda of science is not to be equated with the retelling of scientific thoughts in a simpler language. The propaganda of science is a creative process, since it is not so clear and easy to imagine for yourself and to explain to others just how this or that scientific achievement may influence the development of science, of technology, and of culture as a whole. And yet, we little busy ourselves with the propaganda of science in this sense. In the work of our scientists an insufficiently honorable and important place is allotted to the propaganda of science. Regretfully, at our Institute, too, we have not always devoted proper attention to it. Among us, propagandistic activity took the form of presenting occasional lectures before audiences of scientists, of attracting other institutes' staff members to our scientific meetings, of discussing with them some problems touching upon the fields of science adjacent to ours, and so on.

Such a form of contact between science and life, as seen also at other Soviet scientific institutions, occurs in our country haphazardly. The result of this is a lag in the influence of some fields of science upon other fields of science and a slowness in the penetration of scientific achievements into all categories of the nation's life. We should ponder the question of training our propagandists of science, of organizing their activity. I always try to encourage the widest possible discussion of any and all scientific work. Not only would I not restrain a scientific debate at a scientific meeting; to the contrary, I believe that it is not at all a bad idea to incite people a little, so that they would really argue. We must welcome any discussion of scientific work, and the widest possible discussion most of all. The more of such arguments the more controversies there emerge, the sharper they are, the more stimuli do we have for a healthy development of scientific thought. Pursuing this policy, our Institute perhaps more than any other has sent members to deliver reports at the sessions of the Physics-Mathematics Section of the Academy of Sciences.

Fourthly, let me touch upon one of the most important forms of the influence of scientific work on culture—the problem of the influence of science upon the development of front-rank technology and industry.

In our socialist country, what organizational forms should the impact of science upon our technology and economy take? This question has often been debated among us and is posed most sharply. I must frankly say that I cannot share the moods existing in our country in connection with this problem, moods which are often expressed even by some most responsible officials with whom I have happened to discuss it. It seems to me that the concept of connection between science and technology is often vulgarized in our country: very many people think that each and every scientific research must right here and now be directly applied in technology. These comrades judge a scientific institute conducting this or that piece of research, and whether this institute works well or badly, solely by the extent of the actual help which this scientific work has given this or that branch of industry. This is, of course, wrong. Such an approach is naive and leads to a harmful simplification. Even a cursory study of the history of science and culture reveals that each high-level science unavoidably influences not alone the technology but the entire way of our life.

The Institute of Problems of Physics

It is wholly clear that only thanks to Faraday's fundamental works and discoveries did such completely new specimens of human cultural equipment become possible as the dynamo, the telephone, and the like. But it is self-evident that it is not right to demand from the Faradays that they themselves manufacture the dynamo and the telephone. Faraday had no engineering talent; besides, the industry of his time was not as yet ready to implement all his ideas. Bell, Siemens,[5] Edison, and other prominent engineers did it several decades later. We have many such examples. But the fact that Faraday did not implement his ideas technically does not diminish the genius of his discoveries of the laws and properties of the electric current. Yet, in our country, it is often the custom to judge achievements of science by their practical results only. And so we have a state of affairs wherein he who plucked an apple off a tree is considered the main doer, while in actuality the apple maker is the one who planted the apple tree.

The question of the connection between science and technology has very many sides. When an ordinary engineer calculates the braking of a small cart, or the solidity of a construction, he utilizes the laws of mechanics given to us by Newton. When a patent expert declines one more "very promising" project of perpetual motion, he bases his decision on the law of preservation of energy discovered by Mayer.[6] And so on. When an engineer comes to a scientist to seek advice, either to ask for an explanation of a phenomenon in the production process which he cannot understand, or to tell him how to calculate this or that mechanism—all this is also an important kind of connection between science and technology. This sort of thing occurs in our country daily under most divergent circumstances in tens and hundreds of places. But this is so usual that we do not talk about it; we do not feel this; we value this very little. And yet, this form of liaison is one of the mightiest means of influence of science on technology and industry. But for this influence to occur we must have high-level science, and we must have people called scientists who can be masters of this high science.

For instance, our war technology is at a level equal, and in many respects superior, to that of our enemies' technology. To what is it indebted for this level? It is of course indebted, first of all, to the existence in our country of high-level science and of scientists with their influence, in a number of invisible ways, upon our technology.

To what is, for instance, our metallurgy indebted for its high level? It is indebted, first of all, of course, to the researches of Chernov [7] and all his disciples—to those traditions of the scientific approach to metallurgy which they have created over a period of many years. Naturally, engineers have merited great credit: they succeeded in extracting and assimilating all that was necessary from that high science which was created by the founders of our scientific metallurgy. But without Chernov, Kurnakov,[8] and their followers, our metallurgy would not have of course furnished either such good steel for our army's guns or such excellent armor as we are now producing, and without which our designers would have been powerless to create our first-rate tanks.

Let us take one more example—our aviation. What is the source of its progress? Without the works of Zhukovsky,[9] Chaplygin,[10] and their school, it could not have of course developed. But Chaplygin was never able to design an airplane or even to make a mechanical drawing of its side view. He was a great mathematician, and so also was his teacher, that genius Zhukovsky, who laid the foundations of aerodynamics. The whole world pays tribute of Zhukovsky for his discovery of the fundamental theorem which lies at the base of the calculation of the contour of the airplane's wings, thanks to which the mechanism of the wing's lifting force was first comprehended. But would it have been right to demand of Zhukovsky that he make these calculations and design an airplane? His theorem is that splendid apple tree which he planted, and from it for many ages apples will be plucked by all those who build airplanes.

Certainly, this influence of high-level science upon technology must be better organized than is the case in our country now; it must proceed through that propaganda of science about which I have spoken. We must also better organize the consultation of industry by scientists. It is imperative for scientists to show a greater interest in those fields of technology wherein their knowledge may exert its most important influence. If it is possible to talk of planning in science, such planning should mean the encouragement of the development of those fields of knowledge which may at a given moment exert a wider influence on the development of technology. But it cannot be demanded of an outstanding scientist that he without fail exert his influence on technology by means of a direct implementation of his ideas until a practical result is accomplished.

Let me now shift to a factual recital of our Institute's contact with technology. At first glance it may seem that what I will tell you will be in contradiction to the ideas which I have just stated. But this contradiction was caused by purely accidental circumstances—by the fact that, in addition to my scientific work, I am also busy with engineering problems. But this is of course an accidental factor which cannot be viewed as a rule. It appears to me that the simplest thing to do would be to tell you how the Institute has developed its work on oxygen in industry.

Sometime in the 1930s our technical press conducted a lively discussion of the very important problem of broad utilization of oxygen in industry and the possible influence of this upon modern technology. A number of interesting articles and calculations by our prominent engineers demonstrated how great the influence of inexpensive oxygen could be in industry. Of these possibilities, most attractive was the intensification of crude metallurgy: blast-furnace smelting and the obtaining of steel through oxygen blasting. Then came the prospects of underground gasification, of intensification of a number of chemical productions, and so on. All these attractive and interesting possibilities met head on with the question of how to get great quantities of inexpensive oxygen. I became interested in such discussions, particularly in certain articles which contained evident errors. I began to work my way through various possibilities of obtaining the cheapest oxygen possible. On the basis of modern concepts of physics, it was feasible to demonstrate that the least expensive method was to obtain oxygen from the air, where it is present in its free state. It could further be shown, and I reported this at the Academy of Sciences, that the cheapest way of securing oxygen at the modern level of technology was through the liquefaction of air and its subsequent distillation. Liquid air can be distilled into oxygen and nitrogen, just as, similarly, we distill alcohol from its liquid mixture with water. Then, on the basis of general scientific calculations, it was possible to prove that in modern installations used to obtain liquid air the efficiency was no higher than ten or fifteen per cent, that the existing cycles of liquefaction and rectification were very complex. And it could be further demonstrated that the surest way of simplifying and cost-reducing these processes to obtain oxygen in a large quantity would be to change from the piston freezing machines to the rotary-turbine machines. It is of interest to note that the idea of building a freezing turbine had been proposed already in the 1890s by Rayleigh but, despite a number of attempts, had not been successfully implemented. It was possible to demonstrate theoretically what, in all likelihood, had been wrong with those attempts and how such mistakes could be avoided. All this theoretical work was interesting to do, and it was of course a scientist's job.

Having obtained these results, I spoke of them to engineers, to experts, and I pointed to the way which, in my opinion, should have been followed to create a new technology of obtaining cheap oxygen. They replied to me bluntly that these were professorial fantasies, that all this was much too unrealistic and too distant from their modern concepts. In other words, our technical thought was not then sufficiently mature to accept these new ideas.

In essence, being a scientist, I could have stopped right there. I could have published my results and awaited the time when the technical thought would have ripened sufficiently to grasp my results and put them into actual practice. Today I know that, with this theoretical research, I predicted my own work, the work I have myself been doing these last four years, now as an engineer, but which, as I originally proposed, should have been done by our industry. I had the right to call a halt, having completed this theoretical research—if not for the fact that I, too, was and am an engineer; if not for the circumstance (I will not conceal this) that I was carried away by my engineering zeal. I was told that the ideas which I proposed as a scientist were unrealistic. So I decided to take one more step forward.

In a period of somewhere between eighteen months and two years I built at the Institute a machine to obtain liquid air on these new principles. The general theoretical premises which I had expressed were proved right. A state commission of experts examined the machine. By a resolution of the Economic Council one of our plants was ordered to accept our scientific and technical experiment and to develop it further. I thought that at this point I could relax. Now the plant will start to work out the new installations and to expand them in the same direction. I supposed that, beginning with our laboratory model, which gave all the needed indicators and thus confirmed all the basic theoretical premises proposed by me, industry would now develop the new technique of obtaining cheap oxygen. But in fact this was not so at all. Even though the government gave the plant its rather harsh directives, the plant did not carry them out.

As I watched the state of affairs at that plant, I found it easy to understand the reason for the snag in the development and introduction of the new installation. There were, at that plant, young and talented engineers and engineer-designers who regarded our assignment with much interest. Some of them work with me to this day. And you certainly could not define the attitude of the plant's collective to the new assignment as hostile. The collective recognized the value and the interesting quality of new things, but the plant's staff simply could not get around to doing such new things. They were tied by their day-to-day cares and, above all, by the requirement of fulfilling the plant's main plan. Naturally, our installations demanded much effort, hampered the fulfillment of the plan, and yet, being rather small in their dimensions, played no role in the annual balance of the plant's production. It would be best, I think, to characterize the plant's approach to new and creative beginnings by recalling and somewhat paraphrasing a few lines from *Faust*. Perhaps you remember them. To apply them to this situation, this is approximately how they should read:

> In striving for things exalted and beautiful,
> Alas, we are hampered by our daily routine.
> We can carry out our annual plan
> Only if we hold the higher good as dreams . . . .

Our plants do wish to do their best by the new achievements of science, but life places them in such a situation that their plan's fulfillment is the most important matter to them.

A year's work showed that there was no hope that under the circumstances the plant would indeed, all on its own, solve the problem of inexpensive oxygen. We then decided to change our tactics. The assignment was shifted to another plant, where a separate shop and a special engineering-design office were established to concern themselves with our installations only. By a resolution of the Economic Council the recruitment of the shop's personnel and the technical guidance of this work were handed over to our Institute.

Meanwhile, so as not to waste time, the Institute was doing the work which at one time we thought would be done by industry. From the installation to obtain liquid air we moved to the organization of new cycles, to the construction of an installation to obtain liquid oxygen. We continued to check the correctness of our theoretical premises and so obtained liquid oxygen in the turbine installations. At that, we were also interested in knowing how many hours at a stretch our installations could work without stopping, and under what conditions of work at the plant they would have to prove themselves. Therefore, even though the Institute's oxygen installation worked perfectly, we could not as yet say, ahead of time, that it had grown to be a full-fledged industrial model.

Things went better at the second plant than they had gone at the first one. Still, this second plant found its stride slowly. Even though we were the shop's legitimate chiefs, our intervention as outsiders was not always taken kindly. Within a year or so we had succeeded in building several installations, which we handed over to industry. It is difficult to say just what the further outcome would have been: the war broke out, and so this new kind of contact with industry was ended.

Our experience of working with the plants taught us much. It showed that, in industry, there are creative engineers, indeed; there is a pull toward new technology. From the very first steps of our work on oxygen we met with the government's great assistance to, support of, and interest in all our initiatives. They willingly aided us in all our beginnings. Of course, only because of this did our work move ahead. What was it, then, that hampered the matter? It was the problem of organization, no doubt. Our industrial plant organization is insufficiently geared to a quick and smooth acceptance of new technical ideas. And yet, I do not doubt that, given our system of economy, it is possible to discover and create such organizational forms as would open to us a possibility for a smooth and rapid introduction and development of modern ideas in technology and would give us an opportunity for a broad influence of science upon industry. But these forms have not been found yet. We still must search for them.

The war increases the nation's need of oxygen. Rolling up our sleeves, we have to make an all-out effort to keep working on the machines until they are of the industrial type; we must study the problems of durability, of the duration of the use of these machines. We did this in Kazan, to which city our Institute was evacuated. At this moment, on the basis of the Kazan experience and its blueprints, together with the Insti-

179

tute and under its guidance, large industrial installations are being simultaneously and rapidly built, and these now begin actually to work and produce.

The war, also the nation's forthcoming problems in the postwar period, have sharpened the oxygen problem very much indeed. We have had to act energetically as we endeavored to utilize for our country all the opportunities which our method of obtaining oxygen has opened for industry. I cannot dwell on the details of the measures taken. Suffice it to say that an independent executive authority has been established, that is, an industrial management of oxygen, one of whose main tasks is to draw up and introduce installations of our kind. I am entrusted with the leadership of this organization.

The subject of my report does not allow me to go into greater detail about the tasks set before the Chief Oxygen Office and, created along with it, the Technical Council for the purpose of production and utilization of oxygen. I will only say that the aim of the new organization is to connect high-level science with industry and to try, by utilizing oxygen, to intensify our metallurgy, chemical industry, electrical industry, and so forth.

It is here that I seem to contradict my basic theses, but it is easy to remove this contradiction if we recognize that there exist two Kapitsas: one a scientist, the other an engineer. For the duration of this war the scientist has had to yield to the engineer. In my capacity as an engineer I have concentrated my efforts on the attempt to create such an industrial organization as could be susceptible to the acceptance and assimilation of new scientific ideas. The outcome is difficult to predict, but, in any case, the circumstances of the war demand an application of all our strength to achieve success.

All this of course does not contradict what I said at the beginning of my report. All this stems from the simple coincidence that I am fortunate enough to work as both a scientist and an engineer. After all, cases are known where a man has two professions. Borodin,[11] for instance, was a chemist and a composer. But we cannot make it into a rule and present it as a model. When you listen to a singer, you do not demand that he must by all means accompany himself on the piano. Neither can we demand from a scientist that he should at all events seek a practical solution, that he must implement his scientific research until it produces industrial results. Some scientists do have the necessary engineering inclination, and then, of course, such a happy accident should be utilized. But if there is no such thing, then urging the man in question to do that for which he is not suitable will cause harm only.

Let me cite Academician N. N. Semyonov [12] as an example. His researches on chain reactions and combustion are among the most brilliant and major scientific works done in the Soviet Union. The theory of combustion, the theory of explosion, the theory of detonation, all stemming from his works and the works of his school, exert a colossal and universally recognized influence on the modern development of internal combustion engines, of explosives, and of a number of other fields of technology. In the Soviet Union and abroad, everywhere where they study the processes of combustion, Semyonov's name is mentioned as a basic one. But were Semyonov himself to try to build an internal combustion engine or take upon himself to guide such a construction, the result would be paltry indeed, while his time and strength would be distracted from that major science where he has shown himself such a virtuoso. To us N. N. Semyonov is valuable as a great Russian scientist, as the pride of our theoretical thought, and, of course, his works in theoretical chemistry will be valued for many generations. Yet, as an engineer, he is below the average. And if a singer was not born to accompany his own songs on the piano, why should anyone try to urge him to do so? Is it not better to train accompanists, separately? But we must admit that few are the places in our industry where any activity is carried on to create the cadres needed to introduce a new and leading technology. This, let us be frank, is our great deficiency, and we must fight it. And still it is no less harmful to heap this work upon our great scientists.

It seems to me that we should discuss this sick state of the connection between science and industry, discuss it widely so as to find the healthy forms of this contact so necessary for our rapid cultural growth. In the posing of this problem, we must avoid any vulgarization, such as the demand addressed to all scientists to introduce into industry, by their own efforts, the results of their research.

I will always protest against this. Science—high-level science of large content—has always moved and will always move technical thought forward. We in our Soviet state have all the possibilities to make this influence more actual. But such problems must not be lowered to a primitive level.

The tasks which the Institute has set before itself and which I described to you doubtless exert an influence upon the Institute's structural image. Our Institute has a small staff of permanent scientific personnel, also some cadres of scientists and graduate students who are there temporarily. Only one third of the staff is permanent, while the mobile part of the Institute's staff has reached two thirds. This inevitably has left a certain imprint on the Institute's entire structure. Inasmuch as the temporary staff members are not paid by the Institute, it is natural that, from a bookkeeping point of view, the size of our service does not appear to correspond to the norms established for only the regular or permanent scientific workers. We have often been criticized as overspending, but if we relate the number of servicing personnel to all the scientific personnel occupied at the Institute, then there is no disproportion. Besides, we must take into consideration the fact that the presence of the temporary staff at the Institute necessitates maintaining a more skilled servicing personnel. Graduate students at first, if not supervised, inevitably spoil the equipment and break instruments before they learn how to handle these. Visiting scientists, too, if not attended by experienced laboratory workers, can be rather destructive when handling scientific equipment. Experienced laboratory workers speed up our work, since they can help in the installation of special instruments needed for work at low temperatures, in the organization of the rather complex measurement of deep temperatures, in the demonstration of methods of handling liquid helium, and the like. In addition to its staff of well-screened and experienced laboratory workers, the Institute has at its disposal highly skilled masters who can quickly make special instruments. It must be noted that nothing hinders, freezes, and depresses scientific work so much as a slow making of instruments for experimentation. Therefore the good shop attached to the Institute is of great advantage to us.

And now I will speak of the reorganization of the Institute's work during this war.

The Institute has not found it necessary to reorganize too much. The oxygen problem has proved to be vital during the war as well. The war has compelled us to try to utilize as swiftly as possible all the experience and knowledge gained in this field. We have tried to organize our work so as to make all our experience with oxygen available to industry as rapidly as possible, to be utilized in as full a measure as possible in the fight against the enemy. It has also turned out that in certain fields, too, the Institute's work has a very real significance for the war's tasks. Regretfully, in view of a number of circumstances, I cannot tell you of this in greater detail. Directing to these purposes all the energy of its staff, the Institute has had to curtail considerably its work in those directions of which I spoke at the beginning of my report. We have concentrated our forces almost entirely in the main direction, that of oxygen, so that in one strong drive we would achieve definite and swift results. Our premise is that scientific research not carried to its completion during the war, failing to yield results, may prove to be even harmful if it takes strength away from that work which is more crucial.

In conclusion I wish to say that I have endeavored to dwell only on most general questions of principle as I discussed the problems of organization of scientific work. Some of these are far from their final solution. Regretfully, the question of the organization of science is as yet little discussed among us. Therefore I feel that a number of our solutions are still capable of considerable improvement. But there is no doubt, or so it seems to me, that there are as yet many unexhausted opportunities in the circumstances of our country for the organization of science. Even given such an imperfect organization of science as we now have, our important science already exerts a greater influence on technology, on all our life, than we usually imagine. This influence is effectuated by the developing traditions created by our major science and by its liaison via many invisible threads with our life and industry. It is imperative to remember that without our great scientific traditions, which our scientists began to create already from Lomonosov's time on, we would not have had our good guns, strong armor, and fast-flying planes, even if none of our learned academicians can himself design a plane and shoot a cannon.

We as yet do not understand the possibilities present in our country, we do not comprehend the strength provided to us by the closeness of our science to life, the opportunities furnished to us by the Soviet state for scientific work. We do not as yet know how to utilize that great freedom which exists in our country for the development of scientific thought. And yet, with all that, our achievements are very real.

We are called to perform great deeds in a great country, and we should be the first to value and respect this cause, to care about its development.

3

Problems of Organizing Scientific Work

[*Based on Dr. Kapitsa's article in* Pravda *on May 4, 1957*]

As we evolve new organizational forms of scientific and technological researches, and as we put their results into effect, we should consider the experience gained in the solution of a number of important technical problems arising in the process of the tumultuous growth of science and technology in recent years. It seems to me that this experience shows that we succeed in solving large technical problems with scientific methods only when our scientific research work is organized in a manner different from the way which until now was held to be normal. Insofar as these new organizational forms have apparently been discussed but little and not clearly enough, I will dwell on them at some length.

Let me first, briefly, and in a chronological sequence, list these basic phases in which our scientific work was done on a nationwide scale.

The importance of the impact of science upon technology and national economy was understood a long time ago. At first, scientific researches were done in laboratories attached to universities or similar schools of higher learning. By the end of the last century scientific work had developed to such an extent that there emerged independent laboratories and research institutes. We must note that scientific work in these institutes and laboratories was organized along the definite division lines of knowledge: physics, chemistry, biology, astronomy, and so on. Later came the need to create scientific institutes of a more specialized nature. Thus, from the institutes of physics, there branched off such institutes as those of acoustics, crystallography, optics, and the like, while the institutes of chemistry gave rise to separate institutes of physical chemistry, organic chemistry, and so forth.

The necessity to establish a closer tie between science and technology was felt early in this century, particularly in the post-World War I period. In the industry of that time, large metallurgical, electrotechnical, and other plants began to organize their own laboratories, where problems connected with the introduction of scientific-technical achievements into actual production were being solved. The need for further growth of these plant laboratories led to the emergence, from these laboratories, of large and self-sufficient scientific institutes, each of them active in a definite field of technology. In other countries they are usually attached to large industrial combines, but in our country they are customarily under the jurisdiction of ministries. We call them industrial-branch institutes [*otrasl'*, or a branch of an industry].

In the scientific institutions and in the industrial-branch institutes of any civilized nation, the job is done by a collective comprising many thousands of personnel, and at that they are the selected people—most talented and hard-working. Large sums of money are being expended for the needs of these institutions. The number and the scale of such institutes grow incessantly. A characteristic feature of scientific and industrial-branch institutes is the organization of their scientific work by the area of knowledge, and until recent times such an organization satisfied the needs of the day.

Yet, in the last ten years, life has increasingly begun to suggest the necessity of solving certain major scientific and scientific-technical problems which embrace several fields of knowledge at one and the same time. Let us take, for instance, the construction of an airplane driven by atomic energy. To build it we need atomic physicists, thermo-technicians, and specialists in aerodynamics, to say nothing of designers, metallurgists, and others.

It is customary to define such problems as complex ones. But if we analyze the problems which science and technology now face, we will find that with a few exceptions all these problems are in one measure or another complex problems. It is plain that no single specialized institute is strong enough to solve a complex problem. Usually we solve it as follows: there is always one group much more interested in this problem than any other group. It is this party that assumes the initiative of organizing and guiding the work in question. This work is then distributed, as separate assignments, among various institutes, machine-designing offices, and similar units.

Given support by the central policy organs, such a system of organization has proved feasible in the Soviet Union. Yet it is not difficult to see that this system not only is clumsy, but also possesses serious defects. Its basic shortcoming is in the separateness of those engaged in the work, in the lack of steady personal contact among them. Under such circumstances there is not enough of enthusiasm, of striving for one goal, the ingredients that are so necessary for intensive creative work.

Life tells us just how to seek this difficulty's solution. A number of examples demonstrate that in all cases where, in the process of solving a complex scientific or scientific-technical problem, a united and independent organization was indeed formed, an organization consisting of scientists and engineers of varied specialties but imbued with one aim—to solve the assigned scientific-technical problem and to introduce the results in practice—such an organization has worked successfully. As an instance let me cite the organization formed in the Soviet Union for the solution of the problem of intensification of metallurgical and other processes via oxygen. It is true that here life itself forced us to solve problems of such a large scale by means of special self-sufficient organizations. But, essentially, nothing prevents us from extending this organizational method also to the solution of problems connected with the questions of semiconductors, heat-resisting steel, polymers, and so on.

Therefore, parallel to our already existing institutes of research devoted to certain scientific themes, and to engineering-design offices working in certain fields of knowledge, we must begin establishing large and small-scale scientific-technical institutes devoted to certain problems. Then each such organization will serve to solve a thoroughly defined actual problem. When necessary, such organizations may include within their structure their own institutes for scientific research, laboratories, engineering-design offices, experimental plants, and so forth.

For each such organization to work successfully, the unit must be regarded not as an establishment existing permanently but as a unit created for a certain period of time only—the period needed to solve the problem at hand, be it several months or several years. Inasmuch as these organizations will be of a temporary nature, they can be—if necessary—easily established in those districts where the problem-to-be-solved happens to be most actual, and connected with life's demands more closely than elsewhere.

Such a solution of scientific-technical problems will not require larger funds. But the main difficulty will be in the need to retrain some of our scientific-technical workers, who usually seek stability in the work of their scientific establishments and are afraid to be taken away from such establishments. We must develop and encourage a sense of mobility in our scientists and leading engineers. Such an organization, set up to solve scientific-technical problems, can be imagined almost pictorially as a mobile fighting unit formed by men drawn from various branches of military service. This combined unit is given certain operational tasks, upon the completion of which the unit has to be again reorganized, in accordance with the demands of the next assignment.

Naturally, parallel with such scientific organizations devoted to definite problems, there should exist as before the special-theme institutes of the Academy of Sciences and the industrial-branch institutes attached to large plants and state organs.

The newly created scientific-technical-problem institutes should unburden our "thematic" institutes, relieving them not only of research themes alien to them but also of superabundant personnel. This will afford them the opportunity to concentrate on the solution of problems of greater scientific importance.

It is quite probable, I think, that the principle of organizing our activities by problems will in the future be at the base, not only of the solution of applied scientific-technical problems, but also of the solution of theoretical problems. It should exert its influence on the organization of scientific work at the Academy of Sciences. That organization-by-problem will be effective also here is evident from the fact that currently the most interesting and important problems of science come up when several fields of knowledge cut across one another, when, for instance, biology meets with chemistry, or radio-physics with astronomy, and so on. The necessity of complex work on large scientific problems is confirmed by the example of the recent action by the Soviet Academy of Sciences in uniting scientists on the basis of common "problem themes" in their work. This union not only proved feasible but was also carried out with ease and was well supported by our scientific community.

4

Dimensions of Scientific Work and the Role of the Scientist-Organizer

[*Based on Dr. Kapitsa's speech at the International Sympo-sium on the Planning of Science, at Prague, September 1959*]

In the course of my forty years of work in science I have had an opportunity to observe the numerous transformations that have occurred in the development of science and in the goals of science. Surveying this period of the development of science, we should take note of those basic changes in the attitude to science which are currently a fact. When I was young, I often heard of "pure science," of science for the sake of science. There is no such talk now. At the present time science is being regarded as a necessary ingredient of the social structure, as both a useful and an inherent part of this structure. The state pays increasingly more attention to science as a most important element of the state's very life. Currently, scientific institutions are placed on the same level as other parts of the social organization, such as schooling, transportation, and the armed

Dimensions of Scientific Work

forces. Fifty years ago this was not so. At that time accidental factors predominated in the organization of science. The development of science was then based on private initiative.

Nowadays, with the broadening of the scale of scientific research in all countries, the states' appropriations of funds to foster science continue to increase for both academic and industrial institutions devoted to science. Most complex installations of tremendous dimensions are being built; these are accelerators of many million volts, mighty nuclear reactors, satellites to explore outer space, and so on. The accomplishment of such tasks cannot be achieved by individuals; it is the result of collective creativity; it demands great organizational efforts and means that are within the possibilities of large states only.

As the scale of scientific work widens, science increasingly divides itself into the basic, or investigative, and the applied. I think that in many cases this division is artificial. It is indeed difficult to fix the point where a basic science ends and an applied science begins. This division depends on the aims pursued by the scientist in question, whether they are investigative or applied. Therefore basic sciences are being increasingly concentrated in the academic institutes and universities, while applied sciences can be found mainly in the scientific-research institutions connected with industries. Such a division usually stems from the necessity to finance, plan, and control these or other scientific activities.

In the cases of many outstanding scientists it is indeed difficult to trace just when their aim had to do with applied science and when with the investigative kind. For instance, that very great scientist Langmuir [1] spent all his life working in industrial enterprises; he solved a number of most important technical problems that had to do with the production of electric lamps; yet he also carried out a series of fundamental researches in electronics and vacuum physics.

These days we often discuss the problem of the precise organization of scientific work, which by its dimensions demands a participation of a large and harmonious creative collective. Who should guide the work of such a collective—a scientist or an administrator?

Professor Bernal [2] believes that administrators should play a decisive role here, that they are most necessary to organize work properly on significant scientific problems. I do not agree with Professor Bernal. Organizers are indeed needed to guide collective work in science. But scientists themselves, not administrators, should be such organizers. Let me articulate my thought more sharply by using a comparison with other fields of creativity—with the theater and with films.

Time was when the theater was but an actors' company, and their director was barely noticed. But now, as films have grown to include thousands and tens of thousands of actors, the main supervisory role has passed into the director's hands. It is he who makes the film a success. In science, too, as it involves a large-scale collective effort, the director is most necessary. And what demands do we make of him? Our chief demand is that his role be a creative one and not purely administrative. He should comprehend the sense and the goal of scientific research, and he must correctly appraise the creative possibilities of the researchers, so that he can distribute their roles in accordance with their talents, placing them in such a juxtaposition as to have all the facets of the problem at hand develop in harmony with one another.

Insofar as the solution of each and every new scientific problem must find its own organizational forms, the guiding spirit in charge of an important problem of science must be a man of great creative talent, even if he personally does not happen to be a worker in the scientific vineyard.

I fail to see why the man in charge of such a magnificent scientific achievement as the launching of the first Sputnik does not deserve a Nobel Prize, although perhaps he personally did not do any scientific work connected with this unique experiment. Wasn't he the experiment's organizer? Is it not true that such film directors as Sergei Eisenstein or René Clair, who may be characterized as great creative leaders and who (as all of us well know) evolved most remarkable artistic films, were not themselves actors?

We do know instances where a great actor, such as Charlie Chaplin, was also a great director. So in science, too, cases are known where an outstanding scientist was also a great organizer of collective scientific work. Rutherford and Fermi were, for instance, such many-faceted scientists. But this was, of course, a fortunate exception, not the rule. Doubtless, however, we are now entering a period in the development of science when an increasingly important role will be allotted to organizers of science.

It seems to me that we should forthwith begin a program of special training and molding of men who will be organizers of solutions of large scientific problems. To make these positions attractive we must show great respect for such people, instead of merely categorizing them as a certain variation of bureaucratic administrators. In such a brief speech as this it is difficult to formulate the guidelines of selecting such men, and of teaching and training them. Such men do not happen often, and they apparently represent a unique kind of human talent. We must therefore show them the best of our attention and care.

And so I suggest that one of the tasks of our future is the forming and development of a new type of scientist-organizer, whose activity and significance I have just described. This type of scientific leader is at the present time in the initial phase of his emergence, but in the science of the future, the science of large dimensions, this type will play a decisive role.

The next problem on which I wish to dwell is that of the dimensions that will be reached by scientific work in the future. Let us consider the quantity of resources—human resources, material and financial means—which the state will in time allot to scientific research. At present, even in the most advanced of the states, this expenditure constitutes but a small part of the budget. Yet, with each year, this part steadily grows in both socialist and capitalist countries.

Miscellaneous Essays and Speeches

These days many economists observe large social phenomena in close connection with technological progress. The role of menial labor is steadily diminishing in both industry and agriculture. The press has repeatedly noted that, with the growth of resources of electric energy and with the introduction of mechanization and automation, production will take from man but a small part of his energy: his work will be done by cybernetic machines powered by electricity, and man's creative strength and spiritual force, thus freed, will be directed mainly toward science and art. The question is: what part of mankind will in time be occupied by science and art? Here we can resort to an analogy in Herbert Spencer's style. If we are to compare the organism of the state with an animal, and if we are to pit the weight of that part of the animal's body which does mental work, namely his head, against the weight of all the body's other parts which perform physical work, the result will be interesting. Let us start with an antediluvian animal, say, the dinosaur. He was an animal with a small head and a giant body. We know that in the evolutionary development of life on earth there was no future for such an animal. The future in the struggle for existence belonged to man, the weight of whose head constituted approximately five to ten per cent of the body's weight.

So in the evolutionary progress of human society, too, culture will grow uninterruptedly, and increasingly more means will be spent on culture. We may note here that, as we compare man's spiritual essence with his physical element, nature has given to the development of man's spirituality more generous qualitative opportunities than any afforded so far from the bounty of the state, even the most advanced of the states.

In one of his articles Academician N. N. Semyonov has written that in the future one half of mankind will in one way or another participate in creative scientific work. Thus, one half of a state's population will be carrying out economic functions, while the other half will be working in the institutes, machine-designing offices, and experimental plants, wherever mechanization and automation cannot be used and an individual approach will be needed for the solution of each newly posed scientific problem. Professor Bernal pictures the scientific creativeness of humans in the future rather differently. He holds that each man will give a share of his time to mental creativity and another share to productive labor. Personally I believe in the viability of Semyonov's suggestion, insofar as men who are incined toward creative activity will give all of themselves to it. Humans receive a greater satisfaction from it, and this makes their creative work more productive.

5

Theory, Experiment, Practice

[*This most famous of all the public addresses by Dr. Kapitsa was delivered at the general session of the Soviet Academy of Sciences in Moscow on February 6, 1962, and first printed in the Moscow* Ekonomicheskaya gazeta *on March 26, 1962. Curiously enough, it was seriously emasculated when reprinted in 1966 in a paperback containing seven addresses and essays by Dr. Kapitsa and issued in Moscow under the title* Teoriya, eksperiment, praktika *by the Znaniye (Knowledge) publishing house. The text of his address-essay is translated here from the Russian of* Ekonomicheskaya gazeta, *which (to judge from its content) is not at all emasculated.*]

I

The greater role of science in the building of communism demands a widening of research with clearly defined aims which would open new opportunities in the development of creative forces. It calls for a broad and swift practical implementation of the very latest scientific and technical achievements, also for a decisive rise in experimental work.[1]

The increase of experimental work, as it is formulated in the

196

Theory, Experiment, Practice

new Program of the Soviet Union's Communist Party, is one of the most pressing tasks before our science. The fact is that there is at present a disproportion in the development of theoretical and experimental work, that the tie between theory and practice is as yet weak.

Here I mean, above all, physics and mathematics. It is easy to see that in our country the development of experimental physics lags behind that of theoretical physics. Let us take, for instance, the works proposed this year for the Lenin Prize: there are among them a number of works in mathematics and theoretical physics, but we see not a single one devoted to experimental physics. In my capacity as the editor of the journal *Eksperimental'naya i teoreticheskaya fizika*, I am well aware of the fact that most of the submitted articles are on theoretical physics. The ratio is approximately four or three to one. It is characteristic of the young Soviet college graduates that they want theoretical, not experimental, work as their specialty.

We cannot permit any lag in experimental physics, for this would greatly hinder the normal growth of our physics—would prevent it from occupying leading positions in the world's science along the entire front of most important researches. The gap between theory and experiment, between theory and practice, is a symptom of a serious disruption in the normal growth of science. What we now see in our country—the isolation of theoretical science from life on the one hand, and the lack of high enough quality in experimental work on the other —indeed disrupts the harmonious development of our science. And, it seems to me, this is valid not alone for physics but also for a number of other fields in the natural sciences.

We must take certain necessary measures to raise our experimental physics to a new, higher level. For this, of course, we must first ascertain the reason which is responsible for the slowdown in the development of experimental work and which disrupts the normal tie between the theoretical sciences and life.

I I

It is well known, from the history of the development of physics, that the division of physicists into theoreticians and experimenters is quite recent. In olden times, not only Newton and Huyghens but also such theoreticians as Maxwell usually themselves checked, through experiments, their theoretical premises and conclusions. But these days it is only in extraordinary cases that a theoretician will himself try to check his theories through experiments.

There is a very simple reason for this. The technology of experimentation has become most complex. It calls for great effort during an experiment, and this is too much for one man alone, and so it has to be done by teams of scientific personnel. Indeed, such equipment as accelerators, liquefiers, most complicated electronic systems, reactors, and the like call for a considerable staff of scientific personnel to carry out an experiment. This is why a theoretical physicist finds it impossible to subject his theoretical conclusions to practical tests himself. He has to depend on the experimenters; he has to wait for their decision to test practically his conclusions and proposals.

This is how the disproportion arises—the disproportion between the number of theoretical works and the opportunity to subject them to a practical test. In the course of a year, a theoretician often publishes several of his productions, say, four such works, but it would take usually one year or a year and a half to carry out even one experimental test, and, at that, such a test would have to be done by a team of, say, five persons. It is clear then that for each theoretician there must be twenty to thirty experimenters. This is of course a simplified calculation, but it does show in general that for a proper development of science there should be a better proportion between theoreticians and experimenters than exists now.

Right now the theoreticians and the experimenters are about equal in their numbers, and the result is that most of the theoretical conclusions are not tested practically. Gradually theoreticians forget that any work of theirs becomes of value only after an experimental confirmation. Theory begins to emerge only for the sake of theory, and the best that can be hoped for its value is that it is defined methodologically and aesthetically.

For a harmonious development of science it is of course necessary that theory not divorce itself from experimentation, and this can occur only when theory bases itself on a large enough experimental foundation.

Why do so few of our scientists go into experimental work, and why is this work in our country so insufficiently organized? The answer is simple: these days the toil of the experimenter is far more difficult and less profitable, and not only because in case of failure the experimenter loses time—not the two or three months that a theoretician might lose, but one year or a year and a half. An experimenter's work calls for a far greater effort. It is not enough for him to understand theory. He must also possess a number of practical habits; he must know how to handle equipment; he must create a well-integrated team. All this leads to a situation where an experimenter is recognized as a scientist and gains his degree much later than a theoretical physicist.

An experimenter, in order to present his dissertation for defense, has to separate, from the work done by a team, a part which he claims as his independent contribution, and this claim has to be confirmed by the person who has guided him in his work. It is not difficult to see that basically this contradicts the healthy spirit of collective enterprise wherein participants incessantly exchange their experience and ideas with one another, help one another, and take over for one another constantly. To separate anything as "personal property" so as to make a dissertation creates a factor that is unnatural, that hinders the development of collective creativeness. This causes many people, particularly young ones, to shy away from experimental work.

The person in charge of the collective of an experimental

group is also placed under difficult circumstances. He is responsible for the team's work, but, inasmuch as he often does not participate in many of its parts, it is usually considered improper to include his name when the authors are cited. Young people underestimate the role of such a leader, although it is he who selects members of his team, distributes duties among them, and separates good ideas from poor ones. The leader's role is of course extraordinarily crucial. Under the present-day conditions a person in charge of scientific work is like a stage director: he creates the spectacle, even if he does not appear on the stage.

Nowadays it is very difficult to attract capable scientists to such leaders' posts as laboratory chiefs and institute directors. These posts in our country are often filled by officials possessing administrative skills but none of the needed creative scientific qualifications. And this lowers the quality of scientific experiments, which quality has already been discussed.

In such important areas of modern experimental physics as outer-space research, investigation of plasma, nuclear study, and construction of accelerators, scientific collectives are very large, and the role of their leaders is decisive. Only a correct selection of such a leader can guarantee the work's success.

Let us take other examples. They also show that an experimenter works under more disadvantageous conditions than a theoretician. For instance: if a theoretician is awarded a prize, he alone is the recipient. But when a collective of experimenters gets a prize, each participant's share is very small. In a theoretician's labors a pencil and paper are his tools, and some do not need even this. Thus Euler, on going blind, did his work in his mind.

But an experimenter requires a good material base: premises with all kinds of special equipment, a large assortment of instruments, special supplies, shops, a well-trained staff of laboratory technicians, and so on. The tempo and the success of his work are conditioned by the level of excellence of this material base. Some ten years ago our material base was very weak. By now it has improved significantly, yet even at this point its level hinders the pace of our experimental scientific work, making it less attractive to a scientist.

All this explains why our young people reach out to theoretical scientific work, and why there has emerged in our country such a disproportion between theory and experiment. And this leads to the gap between theory and reality.

We must create for the experimenter and for the leader of experimental work such conditions as would make their labor at least as attractive as the work of a theoretician. And we must further improve our organizational system of scientific work. We must particularly encourage its collective forms. Such encouragement could involve incentives both material and moral.[2] For instance, prizes may be established for experimental work, or easier conditions may be set for earning learned degrees by more than one person for one and the same collective dissertation.

The above, said about physics, can be related also to other fields of the natural sciences. The divorce of theory from experimentation, from experience, from practice, harms theory itself first of all. This I wish to show through the case of the activities of those philosophers who busy themeslves with the philosophical problems of natural science.

I I I

There is an area of knowledge which is generally called cybernetics. Many know just what cybernetics is. They also know about its tremendous role in the life of society today. And yet, here is what we read about cybernetics on page 236 of *The Philosophical Dictionary* (1954 edition): "Cybernetics (from the Greek word meaning 'pilot' or 'director') is a reactionary pseudo science, which emerged in the U.S.A. after the Second World War and spread widely in other capitalistic countries as well; a form of modern mechanism."[3]

It is true that this was written in a book published eight years ago. This mistake has been corrected. But, after all, philosophers should look ahead and see what is coming and not merely record a stage already passed.

Had our scientists at the time, in 1954, obeyed the philosophers, had they adopted this definition as their directive for the further development of this science, we can say that our conquest of outer space, of which all of us are justly proud and for which the entire world respects us, could not have occurred, since it is impossible to guide a spaceship without cybernetic machines.

And here is one more example showing results to which an insufficient understanding and knowledge of experiments in physics may lead. Many among us remember vividly how a number of our philosophers, applying the dialectical method dogmatically, argued that the theory of relativity was in error. These philosophers criticized particularly that conclusion in the theory of relativity which stated that energy is equivalent to the mass multipled by the speed of light $(E=mc^2)$. Physicists had long since confirmed this Einstein law through experimentation with elementary particles. To understand such experiments a profound knowledge of the latest physics was needed, but certain philosophers lacked this knowledge. And by now physicists have caused nuclear reactions; they have confirmed the Einstein law, not on separate atoms, but on the scale of the atom bomb. How embarrassed our physicists would have been had they followed those philosophers' conclusions and had they ceased their work on the problem of applying the theory of relativity in nuclear physics! And into what straits would the physicists have placed our nation if they had not been prepared to take practical advantage of the achievements of nuclear physics?

These examples most graphically illustrate the divorce of certain philosophers from reality, although we have at our disposal a number of other cases as well, such as an incorrect appraisal of the principle of uncertainty in the quantum theory, a wrong evaluation of the theory of resonance in the study of chemical connections, and others. And it seems to me that incorrect generalizations of the same kind were made by our philosophers not only in the field of physics, but also in the field of biology.

This shows that application of dialectics in the realm of natural sciences demands an exceptionally thorough knowledge of experimental facts and their theoretical generalization. Without this, dialectics by itself cannot solve the question. Dialectics is like a Stradivarius violin. To play this most perfect of all violins, one must be a musician and know music. Without this, it would yield false notes just as an ordinary fiddle would.

The work of scientist-naturalists, who made their great contribution to the development of the latest natural sciences, and whom V. I. Lenin called "spontaneous materialists," was done in an undeviating, close alliance between theory and experiment. Therefore, for any further development of natural sciences on a healthy materialistic base, every theoretical generalization must under all circumstances be tested in experiments. A harmonious development of theory and practice is an absolute "must" in all areas of the natural sciences.

As to the "mechanism" itself, the "mechanism" of the connection between theory and practice, I would like to recall an image used in his time by Kelvin. He compared theory, predominantly mathematical theory of course, to millstones, and he likened experimental data to the grain poured onto these stones. The resultant product, flour, is of much use to humans. It is entirely clear that the millstones alone, no matter how long they might turn, can yield nothing useful. So it is with theory when it works for the sake of theory only. But the quality of the flour depends on the quality of the grain. Rotted grain cannot result in nutritious flour. Therefore experiments of good quality are needed not only to construct a first-rate theory but also to obtain practical results.

A high quality of experiments is the *sine qua non* of a healthy progress of science.

6

Effectiveness of Scientific Activity

[*Based on Dr. Kapitsa's speech at the session of the Presidium of the Soviet Academy of Sciences on December 4, 1964*]

The problem I wish to discuss here is this: how efficiently, how fruitfully do our scientists, our institutes work? Should we not direct our main efforts, not toward any further expansion of the Academy, but toward the improvement of the conditions under which our existing institutes and their staffs perform, so as to increase their productivity? Perhaps we will in this way gain more even if we invest in the process the very same material resources. Then the question is: how great can this possible increase of our scientists' productivity be? A precise answer cannot be given, of course, but I do think that in this area we have very considerable opportunities for such an increase.

There are three main methods of influencing the scientists' work to raise its effectiveness. In brief, these are: the moral method, the method of improving the cadres—the personnel, and the financial method. Doubtless, the first one is the most important of the three. The right choice of the direction to be taken by scientific activity, and a good implementation of such a choice, will to a great degree determine the scientists' own attitude toward this particular work. If a scientist may rightfully disagree with one or another of his colleagues when this choice is made, he cannot after all disregard the opinion on the subject expressed by the scientific community as a whole. We must devote more attention to the cultivation and support of the scientific community's opinion and action within the Academy. This is not only one of the most effective methods of enhancing the level of scientific work, but also the chief way of concentrating our strength on those main directions of this scientific activity which are most promising. In essence, this is indeed the real method of planning scientific work.

One of the ways of strengthening social influence is to hold discussions of general problems and specific themes at scientific meetings. Let us admit at once that in this area we work as yet feebly. Those conferences that are rather narrow as to their agenda—the conferences on specific problems—do work well, but the wider the subject of a meeting the poorer its proceedings. The pulse of the scientists' social involvement beats weakly at such wider-agenda sessions. The art, the whole culture, of discussions and scientific debates has faded in our country.

I have repeatedly stated that what we need is a savants' club where we could gather in an informal atmosphere to talk over our vital problems. When I worked in England, I found that the most interesting conversations on the throbbing problems of science were held at college dinners. We used to discuss there problems that embraced many areas of science at one and the same time, and this was the best way of broadening our horizon and of comprehending the current significance of this or that scientific thought.

We must develop social life at the Academy. This was difficult to do in the epoch of the cult of the personality [Stalin's era]. But now we have an opportunity for such a development once more! Yet, for some reason, our scientific community life

205

continues to lag, even though it is not at all in character for us.

An important factor of moral influence [1] is our participation in the activities of foreign scientists—in conferences and other such encounters. But so far our participation is as yet very low. Our delegations are usually four and five times smaller than the delegations of the United States and other countries, and our delegates are often selected in bureaucratic ways, with no strict regard for their qualifications as scientists or for their interest in the given conference. We must improve this part of our work, and we should not begrudge the money needed for it.

A method of intellectual suasion upon scientists, which we underestimate, concerns our journals. A journal should carry on work of appraisal and selection. When an article arrives at the journal's editorial office, the manuscript should be subjected to an expert appraisal, and the author should be informed of the criticism. In other words, the editors of a scientific journal should really work with the author of a submitted article. This is what we do as we edit our *Zhurnal eksperimental'noi i teoreticheskoi fiziki*, even though it involves us in a great deal of detail and is at times difficult, but I consider this work very beneficial for a proper direction of scientific activity.

And now as to the cadres' influence on the development of science. When we at the Academy come to the conclusion that a certain one of our scientific fields is lagging, there is immediately the question of material support for this laboratory or that, the building of whole institutes is proposed, and so on. But we must remember that we cannot maintain all fields at the same high level, and that therefore it is much more fitting to concentrate our efforts on those where we are strong in the available personnel and where good scientific traditions have already taken hold. Chiefly we must develop those directions in science where we are fortunate enough to possess a prominent, bold and talented scientist. It is well known that no matter how much you may support a giftless man, he will anyway fail to produce anything of importance. Therefore, when we develop this or that field of science, our first premise must be the creative strength of the person working in that particular field. After all, our science is just as creative as art, music, and the like. We must not think we will have hymns and cantatas simply because we have established, in a conservatory, a department of hymn and cantata composition. If this department does not happen to have an outstanding composer equal in his talent to, say, Handel, nothing will come of it anyway. A lame man cannot be taught to run, no matter how much money may be spent on the project. This is true of science also. The chiefs at the Academy must search for, attract, and support the most talented persons, and this should be our concern even more than the problem of searching for themes of research.

The institute's director should play the leading role in the recruitment of cadres for the institute's staff, and he himself must be a prominent scientist. But for this purpose he should enjoy wide powers. Generally speaking, our institute directors are nowadays fettered hand and foot in questions of both the cadres and the finances. And as I have already pointed out, finances represent the third method of influencing the development of science. We do have money for research, the state is not stingy; we can get money more easily than, say, American scientists can obtain funds in their country. But perhaps you recall the children's game where the chant is: "The lady sent you one hundred rubles, you may purchase whatever you wish." But then comes the proviso: "You are not to buy anything black or white, you are not to say either yes or no." And so forth. The result of the game is that it is impossible to spend those one hundred rubles unless you resort to trickery. And so it is with the institute's director. He is given an appropriation of money, but he is strictly limited as to its expenditure.

It is also a fact that the director is greatly circumscribed in his choice of the cadres, of the staff; he cannot on his own either discharge or reward anyone. This fettering of the director, his delimited role in this important area, is one of the reasons for the low efficiency and usefulness of our institutes.

Without first lightening and simplifying the work of the institute directors in their role as scientists guiding scientific work, we will as before find it difficult to attract prominent scientists to this work. Right now several outstanding scientists on the staff of the existing institutes (of our Institute of Problems of Physics, for instance) could have certainly headed independent scientific collectives, but they do not want to tackle such tasks. Were the work of an institute director eased and simplified, this would aid a quicker advancement of young talented scientists to leading administrative posts. It must be said, by the way, that the level of our young scientists is higher than, say, that of the young scientists in the United States, where many creative, talented men do not go into scientific institutions but are attracted by the realm of business, which in that country pays much more than science. We do not have any such phenomenon, yet we fall short in utilizing this advantage.

The last point I would like to make concerns the establishment of new institutes outside Moscow. I think this is the right thing to do. From my own experience I know that it is quieter and more productive to work some fifty kilometers away from a big city. But to put this into practice we must create truly good conditions and arrangements, better ones than now exist in Moscow, both for scientific work and for living. This last we have not as yet managed to achieve. This is why scientific staffmen depart from Moscow very reluctantly. And coercing them will not accomplish any successes here.

7

Mastery of Achievement of Science and Technology

[*Based on Dr. Kapitsa's speech delivered at the general session of the Soviet Academy of Sciences on December 13, 1965*]

It is well known that productivity of labor is the basic yard-stick of progress in national economy, and that the rise in productivity of labor is reached mainly through the mastery of new technology and scientific achievements.

When the rise of labor productivity happens to slow down, the reasons for this should be sought in the deficiencies of industry's mastery of scientific and technological accomplishments.

We can see from our official statistical data that in the past the rise in labor productivity has at times reached thirteen per cent annually, but then the rise slowed, until in recent years it fell to four or five per cent.

This shows that at the present time the process of mastery of our scientific and technical achievements does not satisfy the demands set before our industry.

I wish to dwell on the factors which slow down our mastery of achievements of science and technology. It is known that our industry has always been absorbing our scientific and technical accomplishments slowly and with difficulty. This is seen from the word *vnedreniye*, or an effort to introduce, which we customarily use. We speak of "the effort to introduce new technology" and "the effort to introduce scientific accomplishments." The Russian word *vnedreniye* denotes that this movement forward meets resistance. We have become so accustomed to the fact that each new scientific and technological achievement meets resistance on its initial introduction that we use this word *vnedreniye*, and have been using it for a long time, not noticing that we thus characterize the abnormal conditions under which we master our new technology. The word to be used is *osvoyeniye*, or mastery, absorption, instead of *vnedreniye*, which means introduction despite resistance. Once we begin to use the word "mastery" when we speak of new technology, we shall be able to feel that we have indeed reached normal conditions for the further development of this technology.

My experience of many years in this field tells me that six conditions are necessary for the successful mastery of scientific achievements and new technology. I will now list them, and we will see just what is needed to put them into effect.

Mastery of new technology means that industry must learn to do things it has not done before. Thus, mastery of new technology must be considered as a process of learning, and this should be carried out with such pedagogical methods as we usually apply when we teach somebody something new.

When we teach our students and pupils, the main condition needed is the given person's desire to be taught. It is well known that if the pupil lacks such a ready will, you cannot put knowledge into him. Using a stick won't help. But does our industry always wish eagerly to learn something new? Do we always create conditions making it possible for our industry really to feel that it is advantageous for it to learn new technology?

Mastery of Achievement of Science and Technology

For such a desire to appear, it is patently necessary to establish good moral and material conditions. We must create such conditions that our industry, our plants, will be interested in learning new things. They should be made to feel that this is beneficial for them, that it is useful and prestigious. This is condition number one.

Condition number two stems from the fact that when you instruct a man in something new, he should always have the necessary preparation for it. You cannot teach higher mathematics to a pupil who does not know algebra and trigonometry. Any trainee should be sufficiently schooled before you start instructing him in new and higher things. Often we do not take this into account as we begin to master new technology. I know a number of cases where the administration entrusted a plant with the manufacture of new equipment despite the fact that the plant was completely unprepared for this. In each case, such a plant could not carry out the assignment in spite of all its effort. One good plant, for instance, was assigned the making of special metal vacuum Dewar [1] flasks even though this plant had absolutely no experience with vacuum technology. The plant managed this assignment with difficulty, producing many deficient Dewar flasks, and taking several years to master this process. But some other plant, better prepared to assume this task, could have carried out the assignment more quickly and easily.

This is, then, the second condition: sufficient preparation of your pupil.

The third condition, well known to pedagogues, is to avoid overburdening a student. Each plant, each branch of industry, can in a year's time master only a certain number of new things, even when such a plant or branch has enough preparation and possesses a desire to learn. But in our country it often happens that just as soon as a plant distinguishes itself by mastering some production or other, it is at once overloaded with assignments beyond any proper measure. We must remember that an industry, as a man, is capable of mastering new knowledge within certain limits only.

Condition number four is this: when we teach something to somebody, we must create satisfactory material conditions for the pupil. It is not rational to teach either a man or a whole plant at the sole expense of their own inner material resources. For any training there must be a good material base, established in accordance with the task set for the trainees. Simply speaking, we must appropriate enough funds for those who are studying something new.

So far so good. The necessity to establish these four conditions is easily understood. They can be put into effect with comparative ease.

But the fifth condition is less apparent and much more difficult to carry out. It is this: from pedagogical practice we well know that, in teaching anyone, we must first blueprint a clear program of such training. Similarly, when something new is being mastered in industry, we must for its rapid success have a well-thought-out program pointing the way along which this mastery is to travel. Yet as a rule, we pay little attention to this, and we often make such a mastery a hit-and-miss matter. It is sometimes not even considered necessary to have any program whatever.

Two points must be borne in mind when such programs are prepared. First, the program must take into account the plant's production capabilities. Second, we must be aware of the specific features of the new item that is being mastered. Usually the plant lacks a man who can handle both these problems. Therefore, when a scientist or an inventor or even a scientific institute is entrusted with the drawing up of such a program, the specific qualities of the production in question are not taken into consideration. When the plant itself draws up a program, the special demands of the new technology are not taken into account. In both cases the result is a less-than-valuable program.

How to repair the trouble? Life shows that there exists a category of broadly educated engineers who can tackle both sides of such a program. So far there are few such engineers, and we must value them highly. We need these highly skilled engineers as much as we need engineer-designers. Therefore we must help them grow up, and we should afford them an opportunity to participate actively in industry as introducers of new technology. In the ministries and other high administrative organs, special offices manned by such experts should be established. It is these offices that should be assigned the drawing-up of programs for the mastery of new technology, as well as the organizational task of putting these programs into actual practice. As a rule there should be in existence a well-prepared program each time our industry is to assimilate something new. So far, however, little heed is paid to this important "must" in the assimilation of new technology.

The sixth and final condition concerns the teacher. Where there is a pupil there must also be a teacher. We well know that good, friendly relations should prevail between an instructor and a student if the latter's training is to proceed successfully. Besides, as new technology is handed over to industry, its creator, whether a scientist, an inventor, or a team of staffmen at a scientific institute or an engineering-design office, must be interested in its successful assimilation by the plant as much as the plant itself. But are our scientists, inventors, and engineers interested in seeing that their accomplishments are mastered by our industry? What liaison is there between them and the industrial units?

Let me cite an instance where a scientist is such a teacher.

As you know, our laws decree no special material reward for a scientist who is in charge of the assimilation of new technology by an industrial unit. Our custom is that the scientist collaborates with industry as his civic duty, without any extra emolument. This is completely different from the state of affairs in capitalistic countries. When I lived in England, and as I gained my doctorate, being a scientist, I joined a professional association of scientific personnel. On joining, I signed an obligation never to act as a consultant in industry without being paid for it. Moreover, the obligation was also not to accept a lower fee than was proper for my scientific rank. In capitalistic countries this is done to prevent members of the association from undercutting one another's fee. Naturally, our ways of life are entirely different, and such measures cannot be taken among us.

I do not at all mean to say that material rewards play a decisive role in our society, but it is subject to no doubt that moral incentives for the scientists' collaboration with industry should be good. It is necessary to arrange matters so that it would be of interest to the scientist to do this work; it is necessary to create an atmosphere wherein this work would be widely recognized by our society, wherein his collaboration with industry would be considered a useful performance for the good of the state. Regretfully, when you now have to apply to a ministry, you seldom encounter a pleasant reception. All this, of course, does not facilitate the development of good relations between the instructor and the student.

Not infrequently the idea among us is that it is enough to receive an order directing the assimilation of this or that technology, and the process of such mastery is considered guaranteed. Yet, from the above analysis, we see that the process of absorption of new technology cannot be regarded merely as an administrative action. Rather, we should approach this process as if it were "a pedagogical poem." Therefore, as we organize this mastery of new technology by industry, we should proceed by treating men as individuals, eschewing set patterns, and taking into consideration specific characteristics of the men and the conditions involved in each particular case. The order from the higher authority to proceed with the introduction of new technology will, of course, spell out basic details of finances and personnel. But a successful assimilation of new technology rests on good relations between the pupils and the teacher and their common interest in the final success, in the carrying-out, of a well-drawn program. Yet this, alas, is not always the case with us.

And now I want to touch upon another and no less important question: does our science provide enough of a new technological yield, over and above what is usually expected of it, to be absorbed by our national economy? Is our scientists' productivity sufficiently high for this purpose? We must turn our serious attention to these questions. To judge them properly the best possible procedure is to compare some of the data regarding our scientific activity with the information we have on America's scientific work.

It is of interest to note that presently in the United States earnest attention is devoted to the problems of the development of that nation's science and its ties with industry. On this subject they publish much statistical data. (See, for instance, *The Scientific American*, July 1965, page 19.)

Let me cite certain figures of interest to us. This year [1965], for the purposes of its entire scientific research, the United States is spending twenty-one billion dollars, two thirds of which sum are provided by the government from the federal budget and one third by philanthropists and industry. Out of this amount, eleven per cent, or two and a half billion dollars, goes into academic science. From this it follows that the main bulk of the expenditures is devoted to that science which serves directly the needs of industry or, as we say, goes into scientific research of applied themes.

Further, Americans maintain that the existing yield of scientific research is not enough for their industry, given the high cultural level and the presence of free, uninvested capital in America, and that the nation needs a higher scientific yield to satisfy the demand of its industry for new technology. The industry of the United States needs mainly development in entirely new technological directions, such as at one time were represented by television and films, and are now represented by computers and synthetic textiles. The emergence of new fields in technology not only is most advantageous for capital investment but also has a social significance, insofar as it reduces the number of the unemployed and raises the living standards.

Americans feel that the insufficient dimensions of the development of their science are, essentially, the consequence of the shortage of highly skilled scientists and engineers. They consider that their scientific research could obtain yet greater funds if not for the shortage in their country of that type of highly talented personnel who can guide scientific research, which guidance is the main factor channeling the development of science research in a direction needed by that nation. Therefore in recent years we have witnessed the import into America of a great many scientists, chiefly from England and West Germany. In the last ten years, or so statistics tell us, they brought to America fifty-three thousand scientists, mostly young, of whom thirty thousand were men with engineering diplomas; fourteen thousand, physicists; and nine thousand, other specialists. This means an annual import of more than five thousand experts.

When we consider that each college or university in Europe graduates an annual average of five hundred specialists, this means that in the last ten years at least ten such higher schools of Europe trained America's cadres for them free of charge. Inasmuch as the Americans took, of course, not the whole group of graduates from any one school, but rather the best talent from among many, they removed for themselves the cream of the crop of some fifty colleges and universities. The English were greatly upset. The Royal Society formed a special commission to find out the reason for such a serious drain of young scientists by the United States and to decide on measures to prevent this bloodletting of England's science.

Here is what the commission has learned: even though the British and the Germans pay their leading scientists high enough salaries, Americans pay twice as much. And yet it appears that this is not the decisive reason for the scientists' migration. The commission discovered that it is not just the high pay that lures the young scientists. They are also attracted by the superior conditions in which scientific research is conducted in America.

Americans appropriate their science research funds rather differently from the way this is done in other countries. The main funds for this purpose are given not to the scientific institutions as such. More readily Americans donate money either for a definite topic or to certain outstanding scientists, whose work must be supported. At that, the scientists are usually given the freedom of choosing their own topics. Scientific establishments as such receive only a small ratio of all the budgeted sums, apparently not more than two or three per cent. A scientist is of course greatly attracted by this chance to be the independent boss of his material base. Scientists feel that their research can be underwritten in its entirety, and yet they can be given a large degree of independence and freedom of action.

Now let us compare American statistical data with ours. It is not only difficult but almost impossible to make such a comparison, since there is this fundamental difference in the organization of science and its financing between their capitalistic country and our socialistic one. The difficulty is compounded by the regretful fact that we as yet poorly collect our own statistical data connected with the organizational problems of science.

Let us, first of all, compare the numbers of scientific workers. Americans reckon that, beginning with the lower jobs, that is, with engineers and technicians, they now have eight hundred thousand persons occupied in scientific work. Our statistical data show that, starting with the junior ones, we have nearly seven hundred thousand scientific workers. It can be seen from these figures that, within the limits of the reliability of such statistical information, we and they differ little from each other in the numbers of scientific personnel. This conclusion is also confirmed by data taken from a French source. The French declare that for each 10,000 inhabitants there are 23 highly skilled scientific workers in America, 18.5 in the Soviet Union, only 9.7 in England, and considerably fewer in other countries. Inasmuch as we have a larger population than there is in America, this French set of figures also shows that the general number of our highly skilled scientific workers is the same as in the United States, that is, some 400,000 apiece.

In order to ascertain the scientists' productivity we must appraise the scientific output. Of course an exact result is difficult to achieve. Americans try to do this in the following way. They strike a total of scientific articles in the leading fields of the natural and technical sciences, published by scientists in all languages in the main scientific journals of all countries. From such American data we find that the Americans now produce one third of the world's scientific output. Each of the remaining countries produces less than we do. Thus, in scientific output, we are the second country in the world. But if we take into consideration the figures cited earlier, the result is that with about the same number of scientific workers as the Americans, we produce only one half of the extent of scientific work done by Americans. Therefore, sad though this is, we must admit that the productivity of our scientists is approximately one half lower than that of the scientists in the United States. At that, as will be seen from further data, in recent times the pace of the growth of science in our country has begun to recede somewhat. And therefore it is time to ask the question: given the conditions as they now stand, how should we develop our science so as to raise the productivity of our scientists' toil?

Labor productivity in science is ascertained, first, by the range of material opportunities at the scientists' disposal and, second, by the quality of the education and of the selection of the personnel for scientific units.

Let us consider the former: American budgetary expenditures for science grow rapidly. In the last twenty years the rise has been 14 per cent per year on the average, and in the current year this growth has reached the maximum figure of 20 per cent. Science appropriations in the federal budget alone total 14 billion dollars this year.

The leading editorial in *Pravda* for December 17, 1965, cited our budgetary expenditures on science. Next year they will be 6,500,000,000 rubles, which represents a rise of 9.9 per cent compared with the preceding year.

Thus, given the equal number of scientific personnel, our material base is considerably weaker, and this naturally influences labor productivity greatly. Inasmuch as we have no opportunity to strengthen our material base now, all that is left for us to do is to lessen the number of our new personnel considerably, to approximately one half of the needed cadres. In compensation, we must improve their quality. This means we must screen out those persons who by their work will not completely justify the advantages accompanying the status of the scientist in our country.

Regretfully, we do not see other possibilities except a transfer, within the nearest future, of many staffmen who work in science with insufficient effectiveness to industry, where they can be of great use to the nation. Of course, such a serious measure cannot be carried out all at once. But precisely this should be the trend as our scientific units continue to develop. We could, for instance, annually transfer to industry 15 to 20 per cent of the personnel of our scientific institutions, and at the same time take 7.5 to 10 per cent of well-selected and well-trained young ones, so as to raise in this way the quality of the cadres and not to close doors to science for the flow of new forces. But, at that, we must remember that even if we decide to undertake such steps, we cannot carry through into life this measure while the institute directors within the Academy of Sciences operate with the laws and the rights prescribed for them.

We must not be afraid to say that in the last few years the gap in science between our country and America, instead of narrowing, has grown wider. Most urgently we must seek ways and means to catch up in the lag that has occurred. If in the next few years we do not raise the productivity of our scientists, if we do not improve the conditions for the introduction of scientific and technical achievements into industry, the task of catching up with America cannot be accomplished, of course. But if decisively and capably we utilize those great advantages which our socialist way of life affords the organization of our science and industry, then this lag in growth will prove to be a temporary snag only. Deeply do I believe that if we will not fear to speak the truth about our deficiencies and mistakes, and if we will all together seek ways of their elimination, then we will soon again achieve our former record tempos of growth in our scientific work.

We must incessantly and gradually perfect the organizational forms to develop our science; we must improve the material foundation, raise the quality of the personnel, and heighten the scientist's productivity. We the scientists of the Soviet Academy of Sciences must approach all these problems with a particular seriousness. We are the leading scientific institution in the country, and therefore we more than anyone else are responsible for the development of science and the implementation of its achievements.

III

TWO
INTERVIEWS

1

Man in the World of Data

Interview with Academician Peter L. Kapitsa

[*Under this title, on September 2, 1965, the Moscow* Komso-mol'skaya pravda *printed an interview by its staff member* Ye. Grigoriants with Dr. Kapitsa. *The editorial note preceding the text stated that the interview with the world-renowned physicist had been sought, and was now being published, chiefly for the benefit of student-readers, which in this case may be interpreted to mean Soviet students of science and engineering.*

[*Two main currents seem to run through Dr. Kapitsa's answers to the interviewer's somewhat rambling questions: his concern that Russia's students specialize too much, without the broadening interest in general science that would make them truly well-versed scientists or engineers; and his fear that even when they are well-rounded experts of science and engineering, they shun a deep enough acquaintance with the world's arts and humanities, and how could they then be true leaders of tomorrow?*

[*An echo of C. P. Snow's thesis on "two cultures" may be discerned here, but in a peculiarly Russian setting, of course.*

Two Interviews

We may note in passing that Dr. Kapitsa and Lord Snow are personally well acquainted and, on Lord Snow's several visits to the Soviet Union, have held numerous conversations on this subject among others.
[The interview took place, apparently in late August 1965, in Dr. Kapitsa's study at the Institute of Problems of Physics (within the network of the Soviet Academy of Sciences), of which he is director.]

The conversation opened with Dr. Kapitsa's remarks, not on science, but about poetry. He said:

"I have recently come across this observation by a French writer: 'Man needs poetry, but what for I don't know.' Indeed, why do we love verse? Ah, but it's impossible to live without poetry. Why does man place flowers on his table? Apparently, to be different from animals. . . . Right? Man needs culture, needs poetry. But to define precisely 'what for'—this is not so simple, indeed."

He then went on:

"You speak of the world of information, of 1,200 sciences. What is the essence of relaying scientific and technical data? One man provides information which is needed by another. Ball bearings of a new type are invented, or here is a new kind of lubrication, or new steel. What to do to make this latest information available to those who need it, in the shortest way possible? So that it becomes neither outdated nor lost?

"I recall how we were treating Academician Landau.[1] An antibiotic medicine, created in America, was crucial. The question was: how to find it? And who would instruct us in using it? Much if not everything depended on this 'information.' We succeeded. It would be fine if such efficiency became routine in medicine. And not medicine alone.

"Of course, there are those reference journals, a multitude of them. But even their reports are late. Sometimes half a year late, sometimes a whole year. Does this mean that a certain accomplishment lies still, a kind of moribund capital losing its value? Yes, here is indeed food for thought, a challenge demanding our action. It's no sin to learn a few things from [Western] stock-exchange men. They relay information by tele-type. In a few seconds.

"But that's one worry, a concern first of all for society as a whole. When a person is young, he must think about something else: how to become, not alone a good expert in his field, but also a Soviet citizen well educated in many fields. This is largely the young person's own concern. Let us take Stasov.[2] In what specialty would we have categorized him had he been living now? Or Herzen?[3] One must be a cultured man who has a philosophy of living. It would have been terrible had we chosen a path of narrow practicality; had we said: 'Teach me to be a good draftsman or a good typist, and leave me alone.' This is a characteristically American, pragmatic view of education, which does not suit us.

"I am afraid your young readers won't like what I am about to say: I don't quite sympathize with the heightened interest in sport spectacles, such as soccer. Of course, it's better to spend time at the stadium or in front of a television set than over a glass of vodka. But were I faced with the choice of, say, going to an Ibsen play or visiting Luzhniki,[4] I would take the former, I would take *The Wild Duck* or *Peer Gynt*.

"Of prime importance is the entire cultural essence of a given country, the level of social life. In the same way that no real science can exist without a serious participation by scientists in the given society's life, no successful education is possible without the presence of an already educated milieu. And this milieu should demand much. Such a milieu, such a society, exerts a far better control over education than can any governmental office in charge of education. In our country in recent times we have seen a great growth of social and cultural participation. This growth is the handiwork not alone of schools, universities, and institutes, but also of the press, the theaters, the public lectures—of all the media of the spirit. In

225

this respect we do lead, and we must certainly continue taking good care of this. Here any lowering of the level must meet our resistance."

The interviewer asked:

"Pyotr Leonidovich, now that you have already mentioned this, can you possibly expand on your own attitude to personal favorite pastimes, to the so-called 'hobbies'?[5] To what extent do they solve the problem of wide culture, of an expanded outlook on life?"

Dr. Kapitsa replied:

"Difficult to say. For many years I knew Paul Langevin, the outstanding French physicist. He had one weakness: he loved wine. Winetaster that he was, Langevin always said, 'One doesn't drink wine, one talks about it.' He could declaim a whole poem about a full goblet. He was even the author of some slight discovery in this field (I have once written about it) and was very proud of it. How come? I will tell you: he possessed fine perceptions of taste; also he had special knowledge in this area. Just the same I don't think that this was anything more than a mere human weakness. I know one scientist who collects beetles, and another who collects stamps. It is an interesting occupation for each, an amusement. That's all it means, I think. But perhaps I am so strict about it because collecting of any sort is alien to me.

"One thing is clear to me. If a young man doesn't know why he needs, say, [the writings of] Aksakov,[6] if he substitutes some or other *Ersatz*[7] for his own serious self-education, this is a very dangerous symptom."

The interviewer wondered:

"But, comes Communism, higher education will apparently still aim largely at turning out specialists, as it does now. This means that higher schooling alone does not guarantee a sufficiently well-rounded education?"

Dr. Kapitsa replied:

"This is an interesting question. You know what the Collège de France is about? Well, then. This is not simply a university, or just another place where people study. At the Collège de

France this or that prominent savant offers a course for the young people. Anyone who is interested may come and listen. We do this at the University of Moscow, but seldom. Not so long ago Kolmogorov [8] delivered a course of lectures on the connection between mathematics and poetry. Some may ask: but who needs this? Indeed, it is not needed as something utilitarian and practical. But it is a large and interesting subject.

"Suppose, for instance, that Herzen [9] returned to us in our own times. A widely educated man, he [in his time] exerted a great influence on the development of our culture, both political and artistic. How would he communicate his knowledge and his mood to our young people? Where would he be able to deliver his course of lectures? He is not, after all, needed in any special field. . . .

". . . He needs a high-level audience. So that he would be really interested in delivering his course. Our universities should be a place for such courses. . . ."

The conversation veered to the Soviet Union's engineering colleges, the so-called institutes, and their current students and alumni.

"I don't think," said Dr. Kapitsa, "that a man should be chained to the field of specialization he chooses. Generally, it is a difficult question. The Olympiades [10] and the open-door days [11] do not always help [high school seniors] in making the right choice. What, then, is one to do? Suffer all life long [because of the wrong choice of an area of specialization]? No. In my opinion, a student should take from his special institute or university the main thing: the *ability* [12] to study one's subject; the *method* of obtaining knowledge, of information; and a good general-science *base*, such as mathematics and mechanics. Observe that many outstanding scientists were engineers by their schooling. Such were Einstein and Ioffe, among others."

The interviewer noted here:

"An engineer. . . . Involuntarily I catch myself at the thought that my host is also an engineer—an 1918 alumnus of the

Two Interviews

Petrograd Polytechnic Institute. But already for a half hour now Pyotr Leonidovich Kapitsa has been aiming his conversation against the concept of 'engineer only.' . . . But how do you prepare yourself to be 'not just an engineer'?"

At this point Dr. Kapitsa declared that "scientific researchers are being taught by us to do some pedagogical work" as well. He explained that it is good for the researchers themselves:

"By doing this, they check up on themselves: if you know [your subject] well, you will be able to explain it to others."

And of course it is good for the students: "Yes, to discuss scientific ideas with your teacher, to think together with him about various matters—this of course is the ideal school. I was fortunate enough, after having already graduated from the Institute, to go through such a school with Rutherford."

Dr. Kapitsa then asked:

"Why is a lecturer, a good lecturer, necessary, and why is a book, even a good book, not enough?"

He answered his own question:

"Because you can see the man's thought processes [in his lecture]. You remember conclusions that are not as yet ready; it seems that you are present at their birth. From the lecturer you will learn, not knowledge alone, but also precisely how to obtain it. Therefore the beginning courses should be taught, as was true in old times, by the best scientists and lecturers there are. Scientists, yes, scientists should teach such courses. So that the student would find that his very predilection for science awakens—his habit to be educated emerges.

"Do you know what has been said of Maxwell's lectures in physics? He delivered his lectures without notes and often got lost. He would begin to chalk up a theorem on the board—and would get lost. But his listeners insisted that they learned from Maxwell's 'errors' more than from anything else. They learned at the very moment when he would correct himself."

At this point the interviewer quoted a contemporary Russian science instructor that the problem these days was "with what to begin in higher schools—whether with unusually complex matters such as the theory of relativity or with simple laws . . . such as Newton's."

Dr. Kapitsa said he believed that it was necessary in education to begin a course with a certain amount of repetition of simple things. He remarked:

"You surely know that as embryos we repeat the path that is thousands of years long. But we repeat this very swiftly—if we compare this time with our life span. Just so in education, too. It is certainly necessary to know first of all that which is very much with us today; to know the basic and most general laws and formulae. But we cannot get along without history either, covering it briefly, of course.

"I often think about this 'historic' fact: Galileo drops a weight down from the Tower of Pisa. He draws conclusions which, having been further developed over the centuries, are now at the base of the general theory of relativity. All right, Galileo in his Tower—a utilitarian man may again say: 'But for what do I need it?'

"But, in addition to this little bridge into the past, there is also a little bridge into the future. One must look into the tomorrow of one's science, one's special field, to know the unsolved, the unclear, the debatable, to know vistas. All this also briefly. One must not be carried away by fantasy too much."

Said the interviewer: "But you, Pyotr Leonidovich, in your reminiscences about Rutherford, have several times emphasized precisely his power of imagination and intuition. He did not really need his profound erudition to see in radioactivity the process of disintegration of matter."

Dr. Kapitsa countered:

"The simplest thing to say would have been: Ah, but we deal here with Rutherford himself, no less! However, it is more to the point to say: All depends on the nature of the problem at hand. Certain problems call for more intuition and fantasy, and certain other problems demand more knowledge. But no one can tell you beforehand: Such and such a situation will emerge in science, and for this you will need this or that."

Two Interviews

"Therefore," the interviewer asked, "one must develop in himself everything in an equal measure?"

"No, I think exactly the opposite. In general, you cannot set before you some such tasks as, Here, let me get ready to make a great discovery, to achieve an accomplishment. And therefore what is it that I must know? Know everything in a narrow sector of knowledge or [on the contrary] basic things at the meeting points of sciences? Develop imagination in myself, or train my memory? No, you must first of all prepare yourself for that situation where you will enjoy your future work, where you will really be interested as you work on your problems—put all your soul into them. But should you wish to develop anything at all in yourself, then it must be your strongest capability that you develop. At this point, here is what I want to say: It is very difficult to make young people do that for which they have talent. Yes, yes, I am in deep earnest about this. For some reason young people often strive to do that which is difficult. Yet, in my opinion, you must do the thing which comes easy to you. Take our Institute: we have young people who excel as machine-designers. They carry out their assignments easily and with brilliance. This is because they have the necessary talents for their work. But they say: We want to get busy with something harder than this. They are embarrassed, don't you see, that machine-designing is so naturally easy for them to do. But I insist on this ease precisely. Of course, one must be able to overcome difficulties, but one also must know enough not to pile them up in front of oneself needlessly."

The interviewer asked:

"But is it easy for the man himself to know himself?"

"It is indeed difficult without a teacher. The teacher must tell the young man what he will most likely do best. The teacher should guide only. As for work, young people should do this themselves."

"And exactly when in your opinion, Pyotr Leonidovich, must this path to creativeness begin?"

"The student should start his scientific work at eighteen. I have always argued against the categorical 'let him toil first.' We are now abandoning this [physical-toil-first concept].[13] Generally, in education—perhaps more than in anything else— it is difficult to count on learning tomorrow that which you did not learn yesterday. It seems to me that in this respect the work at the Moscow Physics-Technological Institute is organized well. The student finds himself at a basic institute early enough. In the process of his scientific work, which has a definite goal, he replenishes his knowledge. At that, most of his new knowledge comes from talks with his teachers and schoolmates. I have always been convinced of the value of such conversations. Even at the most important scientific forums you learn most important things [from talks] in the corridors."

"But," the interviewer countered, "even the best of colleges or universities cannot provide you with reserves of knowledge to suffice for many years in advance, for all the happenstances of life. This means that one must himself find his way in the world of books. How?"

"Here," Dr. Kapitsa offered, "I would give just one bit of advice: Don't confuse scientific propaganda [14] with scientific popularization. These are two different things (conditionally speaking, of course). Popularization, as a rule, brings science down to a lower level; it simplifies and at times profanes science. It tells you news in your leisure time, so to say. To a certain extent it is useful, but to a very small extent only. But propaganda of knowledge should relay knowledge that is actually applicable, should be maintained at a very high level. Of foreign examples [of such excellence], I would cite the magazine *Scientific American*.

"Now you are a journalist. Of course you do not have to know the theory of groups as thoroughly as does the mathematician whom you interview. But you must know for what purpose this theory exists and what significance it has. Not out of any idle curiosity but so as to be at least minimally interesting to the man you are interviewing, and, of course, so as not to utter some or other silliness. Physicist that I am, I still must know astronomy to the extent that I will use it in the area in which I work."

"My last question to you is about your punctuality, Pyotr Leonidovich."

"I don't like to talk about that. I do often tell how economically my teacher Rutherford spent his time and strength. He allowed no work in the laboratory to go on after six o'clock in the evening. At first I protested, but he said: 'It is entirely sufficient to work until six. The remainder of the time one must think. Those humans are no good who work too much and think too little.'

"One must have culture in one's work. You must foster culture in yourself if you want 'the end result' to be an expert and a human being. Orderliness in your work, in your time distribution—this comes about gradually if you try. Some people are born neat and punctual; others must train themselves into this state. There is, after all, so much to be accomplished in one's life. This must be understood when you are still a student. It is necessary to remember that a machine loves rhythmic work, and that it breaks down when overloaded. We have the same law in our laboratory: Work only until six. We don't compete by speeding. To our most ardent chaps I always say: Do tell me, would Tolstoy have competed with Dostoyevsky as to which one of them would do more in a shorter time?"

The interview was brought to its end when the electric clock on Dr. Kapitsa's study wall, over Picasso's painting of Don Quixote, showed exactly six.

2

An Invitation to Argument

[*Late in 1966 Viktor Bukhanov, a reporter on the staff of the Moscow* Yunost' (Youth), *a monthly magazine, was sent to interview Dr. Kapitsa. The result was published in the January 1967 issue of the magazine, as follows:*]

When I returned to the editorial office from the assignment, a friend asked:

"And did you tell Pyotr Leonidovich many anecdotes?"

"Not a single one," I said. "What for?"

"Really? Not even to start him off? Everybody knows that an interviewer has to make him laugh before starting to ask any questions. Otherwise he would be devilishly bored with you and your questions."

"I am afraid that he did not particularly try to conceal this," I said. "Toward the end of one hour . . . "

"Kapitsa gave you one whole hour? Bless your readers who are now watching over your shoulder. . . ."

My friend's astonishment does not require any special explanations. A man's time is valuable in direct proportion to his creative potential and his civic role. The great Rutherford's

233

favorite disciple and younger friend, Pyotr Kapitsa, is an outstanding experimenter, a physicist of world-wide renown. In our Soviet science his significance is particularly major: he has very much and fruitfully busied himself with the organization of scientific creativity, with the establishment of a rational system of mass production of ideas and discoveries.

In brief, Pyotr Leonidovich Kapitsa is part of a human milieu whose opinion possesses an indubitable social importance. It was this circumstance which channeled our conversation into its main theme. Our talk began with the question of the role of social opinion in mankind's social and scientific progress.

Kapitsa: Five years ago, in a lecture on Lomonosov, I spoke of the tragedy of this great Russian scientist. I said that he could not fulfill his genius to its highest capacity. He suffered because his work was not recognized either in his native land or abroad. His fellow countrymen valued the poet more than the scientist in him. He did not derive from his work that happiness which the might of his genius merited for him.

One of the causes of this tragedy lay in his isolation from the world's science. Another, not less important, reason was that at that time Russia lacked a scientific community. Just as the level of art in a nation depends on its society's taste and culture, so the level of science depends on the degree to which a country develops a scientific community with a civic sense. If there is no scientific community with a progressive and healthy civic sense, there is no progressive science—no matter how many Lomonosovs there may be born.

The creation of a progressive scientific community with a civic sense is a most important task, to which, however, we devote an insufficient amount of our strength and attention. This is more difficult than the job of selecting and training our talented youth. We need for this task a well-planned upbringing of wide strata of persons connected with scientific activity. They must be imbued with love and respect for science, also with the desire and ability to appraise objectively achievements of science and to support that which is truly the best in science. Only such a scientific community with a civic sense, which can correctly distinguish an achievement from a false success, can help science—as it can help also art—to develop freely along the right path.

Reporter: Speaking of upbringing, you apparently address yourself to young people, since to be brought up, to grow up, is the job first of all of those who are young. What atmosphere do you consider the most conducive for the formation of a young man's civic maturity, of his ability to have and hold high principles?

Kapitsa: I can give you an answer, but it won't be my fault if it proves to be rather trite.

Reporter: The letters that come to the editorial office of our magazine daily remind us that the truths which seem so trite to adults are taken by fifteen-year-olds as veritable discoveries and startling confidences.

Kapitsa: Well, then, social opinion that is both authoritative and healthy can arise only in the atmosphere of lively and active thought, in the atmosphere of search and productive creativity. A "must" condition for such an atmosphere is a clash of different opinions, an exchange of controversial ideas, a discussion, a dispute. In the last few years we have made a giant step forward in this direction. And yet, we debate as yet poorly, without sufficient skill and cultural content.

I worked in England, at the Cavendish Laboratory, for thirteen years—from 1921 to 1935.[1] I became a scientist in the course of those years. And all those years were spent by me in an atmosphere of arguments, both public and behind-the-scenes. Most of those arguments were of scientific nature, but at times they had to do with sociopolitical problems. It is difficult to overestimate their value.

After all, discussion is dialectics in itself. In the collision of the opposites the truth is born. When any science lacks opposite views, then such a science is marching to its cemetery, to bury itself. It is easier to ignore an opponent than to argue

235

with him. Yet, to turn away from the opponent, not to know him, to "close" him—all this means to cause damage to science, to the truth, to the society.

It is in the process of discussion that man's mind is sharpened, his opinion is strengthened, and the number of the truth's adherents grows. Discussions should help in this matter of upbringing, of helping our young people in their mental, moral, and cultural growth. And to this end, there is a skill in the job of guiding the discussions. We cannot boast of this skill, not even in our sessions of the Academy of Sciences. Take as an instance the chairman of any consultation meeting, any conference or seminar. He usually minimizes his part to the task of opening and closing the session and seeing to it that the rules of parliamentary order are preserved. But his role should be a far greater one. He should guide the discussion, pose its problems, sharpen the debate subtly and wisely when the discussion loses its fire, and, finally, summarize the gist of the session.

Today's young people should learn the skill of polemics from their grandfathers who made the revolution. At that time the art of oration stood high because on occasion everything depended on words. I believe that young people should foster in all ways possible a frank exchange of opinions, with no fear of consequences.

Reporter: There is the saying that one of any two arguers is always wrong. If so, it is permissible to ask: wouldn't the platform become a source of spreading incorrect views?

Kapitsa: Nonsense. First of all, both of the arguers may be wrong, and then again both may be right. Secondly, you cannot know the truth beforehand. To reach it and to find whether it is indeed the truth is possible only as a result of a contest of contradictions. Thirdly, errors always retreat under the pressure of truths, no matter what handicaps there may be. If worst comes to worst, this is a question either of time or of the number of victims, as witness the history of mankind, beginning with the bonfires of the Inquisition and even earlier. And in the fourth place, let me say something about man's right to make mistakes. . . . I believe that a great man's errors are as instructive as his achievements. I have on other occasions said that errors are not a pseudo science. But nonrecognition of errors is a pseudo science.

It is possible to say that mistakes are a dialectic method of search for truth. One must never overestimate their harm and underestimate their usefulness.

Reporter: Nowadays, this premise hardly meets with any active objections as far as science is concerned. But does this concern science only?

Kapitsa: I don't think so. The laws of development are everywhere the same, and their results are similar; only the pace of the process is different.

Here on my wall you see a reproduction of a drawing by Picasso. It does not at all fit any standards of classical realism. But absolutely everyone likes it. A modern canvas, in my opinion, should invite the onlooker to participate in its creative essence. The onlooker should project the thought further on, should create the painting together with the painter. Looking at, say, this Don Quixote by Picasso, you and I see him in two different ways. We invest the painting each with a part of ourselves. For, thank goodness, there is enough room for this. Of course, such art as this is more complex for understanding than, say, a canvas by Bryullov.[2]

Not so long ago in the magazine *Ogonyok* I read what our well-known painter Pavel Korin had to say about Picasso. Korin has visited America and there he saw *Guernica*, which, I believe, was exhibited in the Guggenheim collection. And Korin has changed his opinion about Picasso. This is very interesting: after all, Korin is absolutely sincere; in painting he is thoroughly orthodox, and here suddenly *Guernica* makes such an impression on him! It is quite evident that a clash of different artistic manners, styles, and creative credos is as useful for the development of art as is a contest of opinions for progress in science. Society stands to gain from polemics, from a candid exchange of opinions. This has once more been shown by the discussion of economics in our press, the debate which played a useful part in the shaping of the [Communist] Party's decisions about the reconstruction of planning and management in industry.

Reporter: By the way, about this economic reconstruction. This is an important crossing-point, affording our young people enormous opportunities. And yet, quite often we hear expressions of worry as to the extent of real readiness of the young people to display their initiative as they are asked to play their role in our economic life. Apparently, one must prepare himself well ahead of time to be independent . . .

Kapitsa: Of course, it is necessary to develop in our young people in all ways possible this taste for their role in society, and the earlier the better. More often than not we see that a man only in his youth demonstrates the bright temperament that makes him a man of progress, while toward his old age he wants to lead a quiet life. Therefore it is not enough to say about the young ones: They are our future. We must say: They are our present time as well. As you grow older, only these young people, your students alone, can save you from a premature hardening of the brain. Who are those that teach their own teacher if not his pupils? Rutherford used to say to me, "Kapitsa, you know that it is only thanks to my students that I feel I am young, too."

Reporter: In one of your comparatively recent statements you proposed the establishment of a scientists' club where it would be possible to gather informally for a discussion of things essential. You recalled that when you worked in England, the most interesting conversations used to occur at college dinners, and that this was the best way of widening one's horizon. What forms of getting together with the same aim in mind would you suggest for the young people of our day?

Kapitsa: To give such advice one must know young people better than I know them. Apparently cafés are good for this purpose, but their clientele must stabilize itself, so that young people when bound for this or that café would know what sort of humans they would find there and what conversations would

An Invitation to Argument

arise. Perhaps it is necessary to establish mixed vacation places for young people where those resting could group themselves according to their interest, as, say, sculptors or architects group themselves. I like very much the idea of combined "camps of friendship" to which young people of various countries come. In general, travel is a must for young people.

Art exhibits should be arranged in various schools, with accompanying discussions, just as evenings of poetry are being arranged (rather seldom, by the way).

Personally I dream of seeing something like the Collège de France created in our country, so that outstanding scholars could discuss with their young audience questions of interest to both sides. This is of course marked by a completely free attendance of lectures. Such a university issues no diplomas at all, but it affords tremendous opportunities for young people educating and finding themselves. Just imagine if Kolmogorov were to deliver a course on the connection between mathematics and poetry, while Akimov lectured on the art of the theater! I am truly sorry that such encounters are extremely rare in our country, that when they occur, they do so by sheer chance. Finally, it may be possible to invite foreign scholars, public figures, and writers to deliver their lectures here, such men as Aragon and Maurois. Why not indeed establish such a school using the University of Moscow as its base, eh?

In short, forms could be divergent; this is not the problem. Ancient Romans, for instance, held their discussions in public baths. The essence is important; without getting together, nothing develops. Such is the basic law of progress.

Reporter: You have devoted most of your attention, Pyotr Leonidovich, to the social usefulness of discussion. I think I will entitle this interview "An Invitation to Argument." And yet in our conversation there was nothing polemic . . .

Kapitsa: It would have been better had there been such an element. However, there are indeed ideas that are not at all subject to argument. For instance, the idea of the great value of arguments.

239

Notes

Introduction. *Peter Kapitsa: The Man and His Work*

1. An official Soviet biography of Peter Kapitsa is in *Biografichesky slovar' deyatelei yestestvoznaniya i tekhniki* [Biographical dictionary of leaders of natural science and technology] (Moscow: State Scientific Publishing House of the Great Soviet Encyclopedia, 1958), Vol. 1, p. 394. This contains a brief bibliography of his earlier official Soviet biographies, also in Russian. A more recent source is Yevgeny Dobrovol'sky, "Stranitsy iz zhizni uchyonogo" [Pages out of the scientist's life], *Literaturnaya gazeta*, August 27, 1963. Most important are pages and paragraphs on Kapitsa in S. Timoshenko, *Vospominaniya* [Reminiscences] (Paris: Society of the Alumni of the St. Petersburg Polytechnic Institute, 1963), pp. 214–215, 256–257, 268, 315; also Academician Lev Landau, "Derzat' rozhdennyi—k 70-letiyu akademika P. L. Kapitsy" [Born to dare—On the 70th birthday of Academician P. L. Kapitsa], *Komsomol'skaya pravda*, July 8, 1964; and Yu. N. Khlopov, "Fizik shirokogo diapazona" [The wide-range physicist], *Sovetskaya Rossiya*, December 22, 1964. For Kapitsa's Cambridge years, see Daniil S. Danin, *Rezerford* [Rutherford, a biography of Ernest Rutherford] (Moscow: Young Guard Publishing House, 1966).

   In English, the reader is referred to "Academician Peter Kapitza Honored With Title of Hero of Socialist Labor," *Information Bulletin*, Soviet Embassy in Washington, D. C., May 22, 1945, p. 5 (includes comment by Oleg Pisarzhevsky, "one of Kapitza's assistants," who also discussed Kapitza's work in another article, "Discoveries in Super-Fluidity," *Information Bulletin*, September 11, 1945, pp. 5–6); also to Richard E. Lauterbach, "Russia's Kapitza," *Science Illustrated* (New York), March 1948, pp. 24–25 and 105; and (unsigned) "Russian Atom Scientist," *Science News Letter* (Washington, D. C.), September 3, 1949, p. 149. On Kapitsa's arrest see Boris I. Nicolaevsky, "Soviet Science and the Purges," *The New Leader* (New York), December 14, 1946, p. 10. I corresponded with Mr. Nicolaevsky,

Notes

a knowledgeable Russian Socialist émigré then residing in New York, and have gratefully used the information he kindly shared with me for my own writings. (See Albert Parry, "Peter Kapitza and the H-Bomb," *New York Herald Tribune*, August 21, 1953; and Albert Parry, "The Russian Who Talks Back to Khrushchev," *Science Digest* (New York), June 1963, pp. 45–51.) In a class by itself, a curious source is A. M. Biew, *Kapitsa, the Story of the British-trained Scientist Who Invented the Russian Hydrogen Bomb*, translated from the German by James Cleugh (London: Frederick Muller Ltd., 1956). It smacks of fiction, although it contains elements of seeming authenticity. Professor Paul W. Blackstock exposes it among the fake books of Soviet "memoirs" done for profit by the ex-Soviet diplomat Gregori Bessedovsky. (See Paul W. Blackstock, " 'Books for Idiots': False Soviet 'Memoirs,' " *The Russian Review* (Hanover, N.H.), July 1966 p. 289. Kapitsa himself is known to have denounced this book as an invention.)

Other, briefer sources are introduced in some of the notes below.

2. Dobrovol'sky, *op. cit.*

3. Abram Fyodorovich Ioffe, 1880–1960, Dr. Kapitsa's early teacher to whom in the course of this book he will refer often and fondly; pioneer of semiconductor, quantum, and other branches of modern physics. Of great value is his little book published in Moscow in the year of his death, A. F. Ioffe, *Vstrechi s fizikami. Moi vospominaniya o zarubezhnykh fizikakh* [Meetings with physicists. My reminiscences about foreign physicists], (Moscow: State Publishing House of Physics-Mathematical Literature, 1960).

4. Nikolai (Nicholas) N. Semyonov, 1896–, Russian physicist and physical chemist; sharer with Sir Cyril Hinshelwood of the 1956 Nobel Prize in Chemistry (first Soviet citizen to win a Nobel Prize); discoverer of branching chain reactions, a new type of chemical process. See Semyonov's biography by Albert Parry in George W. Simmonds, ed., *Soviet Leaders* (New York: Thomas Y. Crowell Company, 1967), pp. 260–265.

5. Timoshenko, *op. cit.*, pp. 214–215.

6. *Ibid.*, p. 256.

7. John Rowland, *Ernest Rutherford, Atom Pioneer* (London: Werner Laurie, 1955), p. 101.

8. A. S. Eve, *Rutherford* (New York: The Macmillan Company, 1939), p. 305.

9. *Ibid.*, p. 313.

10. *Ibid.*, pp. 369–370.

Notes

11. Aleksei N. Krylov, born in 1863, died in 1945. See the numerous articles in the Soviet press in mid-August 1963 commemorating the centenary of his birth, particularly M. Lavrentyev and P. Favorov, "Osnovopolozhnik korabel'noi nauki" [Founder of the shipbuilding science], *Pravda*, August 15, 1963; and V. Gubarev, "Lotsman golubykh dorog" [Pilot of azure-blue routes], *Komsomol'skaya pravda*, August 15, 1963. A comprehensive biographical entry on Krylov is in *Biografichesky slovar' deyatelei yestestvoznaniya i tekhniki*, Vol. I, pp. 462–464.
12. Timoshenko, *op. cit.*, p. 267.
13. Letter from Boris Nicolaevsky to Albert Parry of December 16, 1949.
14. Timoshenko, *op. cit.*, pp. 256–257. The extent to which Timoshenko disliked Kapitsa may be judged from Timoshenko's recollections (*ibid.*, pp. 256–257) of Kapitsa's "indecent behavior" at a dinner at Trinity College where the two Russians shared the meal with a large group of British scholars. Kapitsa "talked Russian loudly, making various remarks about those present." Later, Kapitsa invited his Russian guest for a walk in a small garden at the College. "He orated loudly all this time, and as we were leaving he remarked that this was 'a garden of silence,' and that talking was not permitted there."
15. *Ibid.*, p. 268.
16. *Ibid.*, pp. 268, 315.
17. Eve, *op. cit.*, p. 399.
18. *Ibid.*
19. *Ibid.*, pp. 399–400.
20. *Ibid.*, p. 400.
21. Landau, *op. cit.* More on Landau see interview with Kapitsa, "Man in the World of Data."
22. Nobert Wiener, *I Am a Mathematician* (Garden City, N. Y.: Doubleday and Company, 1956), p. 155.
23. Lauterbach, *op. cit.*, p. 24. Nicolaevsky, in his December 1949 letter to me, warned that Lauterbach's writings should be used with caution: "Lauterbach's information is incorrect, as is much else in his articles." By this, most likely, Nicolaevsky meant that Lauterbach (at least in the 1940s) was too pro-Soviet to be trusted as a reporter.
24. Mihajlo Mihajlov, *Moscow Summer* (New York: Farrar, Straus and Giroux, 1965), p. 97. Cf. Harrison E. Salisbury, "Top Scientist Curbed by Stalin Is Restored to Soviet Position," *The New York Times*, July 11, 1956.
25. Ilya Ehrenburg, "Lyudi, gody, zhizn" [People, years, life], *Novy mir*, March 1965, pp. 109–110.

Notes

26. Wilfred Burchett, "The Man Who Won't Work on the Bomb; Peter Kapitza: An Exclusive Interview," *National Guardian* (New York), September 23, 1957.
27. The full text is given in the present volume.
28. In his writings and speeches Dr. Kapitsa uses two different names for the journal he is editing for the Academy of Sciences: *Eksperimental'naya i teoretichiskaya fizika* and *Zhurnal eksperimental'noi i teoretichiskoi fiziki.* The first is an official abbreviation; the second is the full official title of the periodical.
29. "The View from Lenin Hills," *Time* (New York), January 18, 1963, p. 26. *Cf.* Walter Z. Laqueur and others, *Khrushchev on Culture* (London: *Encounter* pamphlet No. 9, 1963); also Priscilla Johnson, *Khrushchev and the Arts* (Cambridge, Mass.: M.I.T. Press, 1965), p. 11.
30. Zh. Mindubayev, "Chelovek shagayet k solntsu" [The man marches toward the sun], *Komsomol'skaya pravda,* June 3, 1966; also Raymond H. Anderson, "A Scientist Stirs Soviet Art Storm," *The New York Times,* June 4, 1966.
31. Harry Schwartz, "Physicist in Soviet Says Regime Gets in Way of Research," *The New York Times,* April 25, 1965.
32. P. Kapitsa, "Lomonosov i mirovaya nauka" [Lomonosov and world science], *Sovetskaya Rossiya,* April 15, 1965.
33. (Unsigned), "Kapitsa, Soviet Physicist, Is Going to Copenhagen," *The New York Times,* May 23, 1965; and TASS dispatch on the same subject from Copenhagen of May 25, published in a number of Soviet newspapers on May 26, 1965.
34. Dana Adams Schmidt, "Kapitza, Away 32 Years, Back In Britain With Wry Peace Plan," *The New York Times,* May 5, 1966; also editorial, "Kapitza's Return," *ibid.,* May 8, 1966.

Below, in his footnotes to Dr. Kapitsa's essays and addresses, the editor endeavored to limit himself to the identification of only such names as may prove to be of some difficulty to the general reader. The editor thus made no effort to explain Galvani, Volta, Newton, Faraday, Maxwell, Hertz, Bohr, and the like.

I. FOUR MEN OF SCIENCE

1. *Franklin's Scientific Activity*

1. Christian Huyghens, 1629–95, Dutch physicist, mathematician, and astronomer; discoverer of the rings and a satellite of Saturn

244

Notes

(with telescope lenses of his own design); author of *Horologium oscillatorium*, containing the first correct laws of the pendulum and the first theorems on centrifugal force, which in time facilitated Isaac Newton's work; developer of the wave undulation theory of light; originator of Huyghens's principle, which assumes every point on a wave front of light to be a new source of wavelets and a propagator of an indefinite number of wave fronts.

2. Leonhard Euler, 1707–83, Swiss mathematician; contributor to every field of mathematics, also to optics, astronomy, hydrodynamics, and acoustics; originator of mechanics as a branch of pure mathematics; first expositor of the calculus of variation; inventor of topology and nonquantitative geometry; author of the first textbook on analytic geometry. After him are named Euler's formula, Euler's line, Eulerian number, Eulerian variables, the Eulerian constant, and the Eulerian equation.

3. Antoine Henri Becquerel, 1852–1908, French physicist; discoverer of the phenomenon of emission of Becquerel rays, radiations by certain uranium salts; first to suggest treatment of cancer by radium; as discoverer of radioactivity, shared the 1903 Nobel Prize in Physics with Pierre and Marie Curie.

4. Jean François Dalibard, 1703–99, French physicist and botanist, early translator of Benjamin Franklin. In 1752 he published the first French translation of Franklin's *Experiments and Observations on Electricity, Made at Philadelphia in America*, as published in London by Edward Cave in 1751. Dalibard's second, considerably enlarged French edition of *Experiences et Observations* came out in 1756. On May 10, 1752, at Marly-la-Ville, Dalibard arranged, and an assistant performed for the first time anywhere, Franklin's suggested experiment to prove the identity of lightning and electricity. Dalibard and Franklin corresponded; they met in Paris in 1767. See Leonard W. Labaree and others, eds., *The Autobiography of Benjamin Franklin* (New Haven and London: Yale University Press, 1964), p. 279; and Alfred Owen Aldridge, *Franklin and His French Contemporaries* (New York: New York University Press, 1957), pp. 21–22.

5. Abbé Jean-Antoine Nollet, 1700–70, principal electrical scientist of his time in France, chief opponent and detractor of Franklin's theories on electricity. See Labaree, *op. cit.*, pp. 291–292; and Aldridge, *op. cit.*, pp. 22–23.

6. Benjamin Wilson of London, who objected to placing pointed lightning rods on powder magazines, and of whom Franklin wrote on March 20, 1773: "Mr. Wilson is grown angry that his advice was not followed in making them blunt for the public

245

Notes

magazines of gunpowder, and has published a pamphlet, reflecting on the Royal Society, the committee, and myself, with some asperity, and endeavoring to alarm the city with the supposed danger of pointed rods drawing the lightning into them and blowing them up." See John Bigelow, ed., *The Works of Benjamin Franklin*, (New York and London: G. P. Putnam's Sons, 1904), Vol. 6, p. 99.

7. Mikhail Lomonosov is the subject of Dr. Kapitsa's next essay in this book. Georg Wilhelm Rikhman (Richman), 1711–53, Russian physicist of Baltic German origin; pioneer researcher in heat and electricity; close collaborator of Lomonosov; killed by lightning during an experiment.

8. Charles Augustin de Coulomb, 1736–1806, French physicist; celebrated for his researches on torsion; inventor of a torsion balance for measuring the force of magnetic and electrical attraction; inventor of a magnetoscope and a magnetometer; author of Coulomb's law on interaction of two electrical charges of certain magnitudes. After him, coulomb, the unit of the static quantity of electricity, is named.

9. Karl Friedrich Gauss, 1777–1855, German mathematician and astronomer, after whom gauss, a unit of magnetic induction, is named; developer (in mathematical statistics) of the theory of errors, the method of least squares, and the frequency curve or function (known as the Gaussian error, normal, or probability curve); formulator of the laws of terrestrial magnetism; author of work on curves and surfaces which cleared the way for a curved space time.

10. Marquis Pierre Simon de Laplace, 1749–1827, French astronomer and mathematician; discoverer of the planetary mean motions; author of the laws of motion of Jupiter's and Saturn's satellites; researcher on the consequences of the law of universal gravitation.

11. Simeon Denis Poisson, 1781–1840, French mathematician and physicist; author of significant researches in definite integrals; originator of ideas relating mathematics to physics, particularly in electrostatics and magnetism.

12. Henry Cavendish, 1731–1810, British physicist and chemist; first to determine the real nature of an extremely buoyant gas, which he called "inflammable air," but which later was named hydrogen by Antoine Lavoisier (because it burned water); first to isolate the gas later called argon (credit for its definite discovery, however, went in 1894 to John Rayleigh and William Ramsay); discoverer of nitric acid and pioneer in determining

the specific gravity of carbon dioxide; originator of the Cavendish experiment for ascertaining the earth's density.

13. Georg Simon Ohm, 1787–1854, German physicist, author of Ohm's law in electricity relating to voltage and current. After him also ohm, the electrical unit of resistance, is named.

2. *Lomonosov and the World of Science*

1. Alexander N. Radishchev, 1749–1802, Russian radical philosopher and poet, exiled by Empress Catherine II to Siberia for his writings; ended his life by suicide.
2. Alexander S. Pushkin, 1799–1837, Russia's foremost poet, prose writer, and playwright; killed in a duel over the honor of his wife (who certainly was not worth this great sacrifice).
3. Vissarion G. Belinsky, 1811–48, Russian radical philosopher and literary critic; died of tuberculosis just as the police of Tsar Nicholas I were getting ready to arrest him.
4. Nicholas A. Dobrolyubov, 1836–61, Russia radical literary critic and political writer.
5. Nicholas G. Chernyshevsky, 1828–89, Russian radical literary critic and political writer, of great influence upon Vladimir Lenin.
6. Alexander I. Herzen (Gertsen), 1812–70, Russian revolutionary leader (in West European exile), philosopher, and writer.
7. Dmitry I. Pisarev, 1840–68, Russian literary critic.
8. Konstantin S. Aksakov, 1817–60, Russian writer (son of the more famous writer Sergei T. Aksakov), who wrote on Lomonosov's place in the history of the Russian language and literature.
9. Boris N. Menshutkin, 1874–1938, Russian chemist and historian of chemistry; the most outstanding Russian biographer of Lomonosov.
10. Pavel I. Val'den (Walden), 1863–1957, Baltic German chemist who left Russia for Germany after the revolution of 1917. It took courage for Dr. Kapitsa to give Val'den this friendly mention, since the official Soviet press has attacked Val'den as a pernicious émigré.
11. Sergei I. Vavilov, 1891–1951, Russian physicist, president of the Soviet Academy of Sciences, 1945–51.
12. Alexander Ye. Fersman, 1883–1945, Russian mineralogist and geochemist; cofounder (with Vladimir I. Vernadsky) of geochemistry in Russia.

Notes

13. Vladimir L. Komarov, 1869–1945, Russian botanist and geographer.
14. Ivan P. Martos, 1752–1835, Russian sculptor of Ukrainian Cossack origin. Famous for his monument to Minin and Pozharsky, saviors of Russia during her "Time of Troubles" (early seventeenth century), now standing in Red Square in Moscow.
15. Fedot I. Shubin (Shubnoy), 1740–1805, Russian sculptor-portraitist, of peasant origin, hailing from Lomonosov's own White Sea shore, and Lomonosov's personal protégé.
16. Count Ivan I. Shuvalov, 1727–97, a lover of Empress Elizabeth of Russia; founder and first curator of the University of Moscow; a special patron of science and art, particularly of Lomonosov personally.
17. Count Michael I. Vorontsov, 1714–67, Russian statesman; participant in the palace revolution of 1741 which made Elizabeth, the daughter of Peter the Great, empress of Russia; chancellor of Russia, 1758–63.
18. Count Gregory G. Orlov, 1734–83, Russian officer of the guards who headed the palace revolution of 1762 which made Catherine II the empress of Russia; a lover of Catherine.
19. See Note 2 to Dr. Kapitsa's address on Benjamin Franklin.
20. Daniel Bernulli, 1700–82. Swiss scientist researching in mathematics, physics, mechanics, hydrodynamics, physiology, and medicine; actively occupied at the St. Petersburg Academy of Sciences, 1725–33, and contributing to its publications until 1778.
21. In English, see Boris Menshutkin's book, *Russia's Lomonosov, Chemist, Courtier, Physicist, Poet*, published in 1952 by the Princeton University Press for the Russian Translation Project of the American Council of Learned Societies.
22. Christian Wolff (Wolf), 1679–1754, German philosopher and mathematician, known for his contribution to idealistic metaphysics, for which in due time Friedrich Engels attacked him mercilessly.
23. Ernst Johann Biron (Buehren), 1690–1772, officially chamberlain to Russia's Empress Anna, but actually ruler of that country from 1730 to 1740; deposed and exiled to Siberia, 1740–62.
24. Kirill G. Razumovsky, 1728–1803, the last hetman of the Ukraine, a powerful member of the court of Russia's Empress Elizabeth. From 1746 to 1765, despite his youth and lack of education, he was president of the Russian Academy of Sciences because his brother Aleksei was a lover (and according to some accounts, a secret husband) of Empress Elizabeth.
25. In imperial Russian times, it was customary to make a state

holiday of each anniversary of the current sovereign's coronation. In this case Count Razumovsky meant the celebration, on a proper day in 1753, of the anniversary of the coronation of Empress Elizabeth who ascended the throne in 1741.

26. Sir Humphry Davy, 1778–1829, British chemist; noted for his research on laughing gas; successful at isolation of potassium and sodium (1807), and of calcium, barium, boron, magnesium, and strontium (1808); inventor of a safety lamp for miners.

27. Anton van Leeuwenhoek, 1632–1723, Dutch naturalist and microscope-maker; gave the first complete description of bacteria, protozoa, and red blood cells.

28. Peter N. Lebedev, 1866–1912, Russian physicist; pioneer in atomic studies, electromagnetic wave research, and cosmic-ray investigation.

29. Dmitry S. Rozhdestvensky, 1876–1940, Russian physicist; contributor to the theory and systematization of spectra of atoms.

30. Peter P. Lazarev, 1878–1942, Russian physicist; researcher in molecular physics; pioneer of biophysics.

31. See Note 3 to "Introduction. Peter Kapitsa: The Man and His Work."

3a. *Reminiscences about Professor Ernest Rutherford*

1. Lord John William Strutt Rayleigh, 1842–1919, British physicist; winner of the 1904 Nobel Prize in Physics; co-discoverer of argon (with Sir William Ramsay, 1894); author of important findings on sound and light.

2. Sir Joseph John Thomson, 1856–1940, British physicist; winner of the 1906 Nobel Prize in Physics for his researches on conduction of electricity through gases; discoverer in 1897 of the electron.

3. Sir John Frederick William Herschel, 1792–1871, British astronomer and philosopher; discoverer and measurer of many hitherto unseen clusters of stars and nebulae; son of Sir William Herschel, 1738–1822, celebrated pioneer in the study of the stars in space.

4. William Thomson Kelvin, 1824–1907, British physicist and mathematician, noted for his work in thermodynamics; author of the Kelvin scale of temperature (the absolute scale with the absolute zero).

5. John Dalton, 1766–1844, British chemist and physicist; pioneer

Notes

of atomic studies; author of Dalton's law of partial pressures.

6. John Alexander McClelland, 1870–1920, Irish physicist; from 1900 professor of experimental physics at University College in Dublin, where he researched in electrons.

7. Sir John Sealy Edward Townsend, 1868–1957, Irish physicist; researcher in electrons and the ionization of gases. At Cambridge he made the first direct determination of the elementary ionic charge.

8. Paul Langevin, 1872–1946, French physicist and chemist; subject of Dr. Kapitsa's personal reminiscences (see pp. 140–150 of this book).

9. Frederick Soddy, 1877–1956, British chemist; winner of the 1921 Nobel Prize in Chemistry for his researches and discoveries in radioactivity.

10. James Prescott Joule, 1818–89, British physicist; pioneer in determining the mechanical equivalent of heat; contributor of important findings also in the fields of electricity and thermodynamics.

11. Hans Geiger, 1882–1945, German physicist; designer of the Geiger counter, an instrument to detect radioactivity (1908–13); redesigned with A. Mueller (1928).

12. Sir James Chadwick, 1891–, British physicist; winner of the 1935 Nobel Prize in Physics for his 1932 discovery of the neutron.

13. Sir John Douglas Cockcroft, 1897–1967, British physicist; sharer with E. T. S. Walton of the 1951 Nobel Prize in Physics for their pioneer accomplishments in atomic acceleration; head of Britain's first atomic research center at Harwell. Ernest Thompson Walton, 1903–, Irish physicist; co-winner with J. D. Cóckcroft of the 1951 Nobel Prize in Physics.

14. Sir William Crookes, 1832–1919, British chemist and physicist; discoverer of the element thallium and cathode rays. After him Crookes' space is named—the dark space in a vacuum between the cathode and the negative glow, the result of a very low pressure.

15. Sir Ernest Marsden, 1889–, British physicist; researcher on diffuse reflection of the alpha particles; discoverer (in 1914, at Manchester) of important effects of the projection of alpha rays into hydrogen, which discovery helped Rutherford in his nuclear work. In 1915 he was appointed professor of physics in Victoria College, Wellington, and from then on spent years of research and teaching in New Zealand.

16. Dr. Kapitsa seems to have taken, at various times, somewhat different approaches to the question of whether or not Ruther-

ford was to be considered a man of extraordinary intuition. Early in his acquaintance with Rutherford, in 1921–22, he wrote to his mother: "His mind is absolutely unique: a colossal sensitivity, intuition," and, "He has a devilish intuition." (See later in this book, "The First Two and a Half Years with Rutherford— Young Kapitsa Writes to His Mother.") But in his 1937 speech Dr. Kapitsa spoke of Rutherford's intuition in a different way— he appeared to wish avoiding an acknowledgment of Rutherford's keen intuition in words that might make the great man's accomplishments seem somehow less great, perhaps even easily come by. And so in 1937, immediately after Rutherford's death, and emotionally affected by it, Kapitsa made a point of qualifying the idea that Rutherford was a man of unusual intuition. In his speech of 1937 Kapitsa said that the matter of any man's intuition "may be true in part only, that in any case there is a large exaggeration in this." He called intuition "some sort of unconscious process," implied that there was something too easy in having an intuition, and contrasted it with "deep thinking." But in his speech of 1966 (see in this book "More Recollections about Rutherford"), Dr. Kapitsa once more changed his ideas on intuition, now defining it as not an "unconscious process" but a "thinking process," a "mighty process of creative thinking." Intuition and thinking were now, in 1966, in Kapitsa's mind, far more closely allied. Between 1937 and 1966 he had read Freud, and this perhaps was the reason for the change.

17. Walther Bothe, 1891–1957, German physicist; in World War II helped the notably unsuccessful Nazi efforts in the development of nuclear physics; co-winner with Max Born of the 1954 Nobel Prize in Physics for their researches in quantum mechanics.

18. This passage may be found in Sir James Chadwick, ed., *The Collected Papers of Lord Rutherford of Nelson* (New York: Interscience Publishers, 1965), Vol. 3, p. 34.

19. Sir Arthur Stanley Eddington, 1882–1944, British physicist and astronomer, who in his philosophical lack of responsibility once ventured an opinion that electrons may be "only a mental concept" and in reality do not exist, thereby arousing Rutherford's indignation.

20. Henry G. J. Moseley, 1887–1915, British physicist; at a young age author of important discoveries in his studies of X-ray spectra of elements; killed at the age of twenty-eight at Gallipoli in World War I. (In his text Dr. Kapitsa gave Moseley's age at death as twenty-seven.)

21. Sir George Howard Darwin, 1845–1912 (second son of Charles Darwin), British astronomer and mathematician; as a professor

Notes

at Cambridge noted for his research and findings in cosmogony.

22. Dr. Kapitsa seems to be in error here: no Robertson was at Manchester with Rutherford, but there was Harold Roper Robinson, 1889–1955, British physicist, who had a long and distinguished career in researches and publications on radioactivity, Roentgen rays, and atomic structure. At the University of Manchester, Robinson was lecturer and assistant director of physical laboratories.

23. Sir Mark Oliphant, 1901—, British physicist; assistant director of research at the Cavendish Laboratory in 1935; authority on electricity in gases and on nuclear physics.

24. Patrick Maynard Stuart Blackett, 1897—, British physicist; winner of the 1948 Nobel Prize in Physics for his work on cosmic rays and his improvement of the Wilson cloud chamber; author of books on atomic weapons and their military and political consequences; president of the Royal Society since 1965.

25. Sir Charles Drummond Ellis, 1895—, British physicist; coauthor with Rutherford and James Chadwick of *Radiations from Radioactive Substances* (1930).

26. George Hugh Henderson, 1892–1949, British physicist, who in 1922 reported on his experiments in radioactivity wherein he "fired in a high vacuum the alpha rays from a speck of radium through a small hole in a metal sheet and deflected them by a magnetic field," which impressed Rutherford very much (A. S. Eve, *op. cit.*, pp. 293–294). Henderson left for Canada that year (1922), where he researched and lectured at the University of Saskatchewan (1922–24) and at Dalhousie University, Halifax (1924–49).

3b. More Recollections about Rutherford

1. G. R. Crowe. For intimate glimpses of his work with Rutherford, see Eve, *op. cit.*, pp. 291 and 413.

2. Robert Andrews Millikan, 1868–1953, U.S. physicist; winner of the 1923 Nobel Prize in Physics for his work on the electron; author of important studies on cosmic rays and physical and electric constants.

3. Otto Stern, 1888—, German-American physicist; fled Nazi Germany in 1933 and came to the United States; winner of the 1943 Nobel Prize in Physics for his contributions to the atomic-ray method and his discovery of the magnetic moment of the proton.

4. James Franck, 1882–1946, German-American physicist; came to the United States in 1935; sharer with Gustav Hertz of the 1925 Nobel Prize in Physics for their work on the impact of the electron on the atom.
5. Max Born, 1882–, German-British physicist, who was forced out of Germany by the Nazis and came to England; sharer with Walther Bothe of the 1954 Nobel Prize in Physics for their researches in quantum mechanics.
6. Leo Szilard, 1898–1964, Hungarian-American nuclear physicist, on whose initiative early in World War II Albert Einstein wrote his famous letter to the United States President Franklin D. Roosevelt, which led to the establishment of the "Manhattan Project" resulting in the first atomic bomb. After the war, Szilard left nuclear physics for biophysics, and passionately worked in the movement to ban nuclear warfare.
7. Hendrik Anton Lorentz, 1853–1928, Dutch physicist; one of the first to presume the existence of electrons; sharer with Pieter Zeeman of the 1902 Nobel Prize in Physics.
8. The fact that Ehrenfest did, later in the same year 1933, commit suicide tends somewhat to undermine this rather extravagant praise by Kapitsa of Rutherford's powers in "complex psychological situations." A more detailed account of Ehrenfest's life, work, and death is in the already cited book by Abram F. Ioffe, *Vstrechi s fizikami* (see Note 3 to "Introduction. Peter Kapitsa: The Man and His Work"), chapter III, "Pavel Sigismundovich Ehrenfest," pp. 38–44.
9. Daniil Danin, Rutherford's Russian biographer, states that the letter was written by the pupils of the Kiev School 79. (See Danin, *op. cit.*, p. 595.)

3c. *The First Two and a Half Years with Rutherford—Young Kapitsa Writes to His Mother*

1. "We" means Kapitsa's fellow members of the delegation of the Academy of Sciences sent to Western Europe to renew scientific contacts and purchase scientific equipment, most notably Professor Abram Ioffe and Aleksei Krylov (Kapitsa's future father-in-law). Ioffe is definitely known to have traveled with Kapitsa to Cambridge to meet Rutherford.
2. Apparently Kapitsa expected another winter of privation were he to return to Petrograd instead of staying in England.

Notes

3. Here Kapitsa seems to refer to the memory of his first wife and their two children. See page 4 of this book.
4. A practicum was a kind of minor, dry-run work for a new junior member at a European laboratory at the time. Danin remarks that at Cavendish everyone started with about six months of a practicum in radioactivity in the attic of the laboratory, but that Kapitsa was kept at this for two weeks only.
5. "We" may mean a companion on that wild motorcycle ride (see farther down, letter of January 17, 1922), but it may also be a self-mocking, pseudo royal "we."
6. Danin remarks that this must have been "Dr. Shimizu, who soon left for his native land."
7. Danin identifies this American as Henry D. Smyth, 1898—, in time famous for the very first (1945) description of the atom bomb.
8. Irving Langmuir, 1881–1957, U. S. chemist; winner of the 1932 Nobel Prize in Chemistry for his contributions in surface chemistry.
9. Jean Baptiste Perrin, 1870–1942, French physicist; an early researcher in nuclear physics; winner of the 1926 Nobel Prize in Physics for his work leading to an accurate calculation of the size of atoms.
10. For the origin of this nickname given by Kapitsa to Rutherford, see page 8 of this book.
11. "All right" was written by Kapitsa in English.
12. One verst, an old-fashioned Russian measure of distance, equals 3,500 feet.
13. This may be a retelling of his accident described in the letter of August 16, 1921, and yet again it may be a second such accident.
14. Danin remarks that this was P. M. S. Blackett, "three years Kapitsa's junior."
15. Danin explains that the idea was to place C. T. R. Wilson's expansion chamber into a strong magnetic field, so as to observe the distortion of the mist tracks formed there by alpha particles.
16. Sir Ralph Howard Fowler, 1889–1944, British mathematician; since 1914 fellow of Trinity College, Cambridge; from 1932 professor of applied mathematics at the University of Cambridge; in 1921 married Eileen Mary, Rutherford's only child, who died in 1930.
17. G. I. Taylor, of whom no other information could be discovered except that he was a friend of Rutherford's with whom he regularly played golf at Cambridge (Eve, *op. cit.*, p. 409).

Notes

18. Francis William Aston, 1877–1945, British physicist and chemist, with the Cavendish Laboratory since 1910; winner of the 1922 Nobel Prize in Chemistry for his discovery of isotopes in non-radioactive elements.
19. Danin identifies these two as John D. Cockcroft and W. Webster.
20. A chummy name for Nicholas, in this instance for Nicholas Semyonov, Kapitsa's friend of Petrograd days. See Note 4 to "Introduction. Peter Kapitsa: The Man and His Work."
21. Kapitsa's laboratory assistant.
22. Pieter Zeeman, 1865–1943, Dutch physicist; sharer with Hendrick Lorentz of the 1902 Nobel Prize in Physics; discoverer of the Zeeman effect produced on the spectrum of a light beam resulting from its passage through a magnetic field.
23. Lord Robert John Strutt Rayleigh, 1875–1946, British physicist, son of the famous Lord John William Strutt Rayleigh (winner of the 1904 Nobel Prize in Physics; see Note 1 to "Reminiscences About Professor Ernest Rutherford"). The son wrote biographies of his father (1924) and of Sir J. J. Thomson (1942).
24. This was the so-called Kapitsa Discussion Club, in which Cockcroft, Blackett, Oliphant, and others participated.
25. Danin explains these as Kapitsa's "famous experiments in creating strong magnetic fields, of short duration, yet unprecedented in their tension." Danin adds: "These experiments were dangerous because destructive overloading occurred in the installation."

4. Paul Langevin, Physicist and Civic Leader

1. Prince Louis Victor de Broglie, 1892–, French physicist; winner of the 1929 Nobel Prize in Physics for his 1924 theory of the wave character of electrons.
2. This most likely means Frédéric Joliot-Curie, 1900–58, rather than his wife Irène (elder daughter of Pierre and Marie Curie), 1897–1956, the French physicists who shared the 1935 Nobel Prize in Chemistry (the third Nobel Prize to be awarded to the the family).
3. Ludwig Boltzmann, 1844–1906, Austrian physicist; important contributor to statistical mechanics and to the kinetic theory of gases; coauthor of the Stefan-Boltzmann law on radiation from a black body.
4. Wilhelm Ostwald, 1853–1932, German physical chemist and

Notes

natural philosopher; winner of the 1909 Nobel Prize in Chemistry for work on catalysts and his research into the fundamental principles governing equilibrium and rates of reaction.

5. Paul A. M. Dirac, 1902—, British physicist; co-winner with Erwin Schroedinger of the 1933 Nobel Prize in Physics for their work on the quantum theory, especially wave mechanics. In 1928 Dirac evolved a theory of the electron, and in 1931 he predicted the existence of the positron. His contributions have been in the areas of electromagnetic fields and elementary particles as well as the quantum theory.

6. Erwin Schroedinger, 1887–1961, Austrian physicist; sharer with Dirac of the 1933 Nobel Prize in Physics; author of the Schroedinger equation, which is the fundamental equation of modern physics replacing Newtonian mechanics in the description of atomic phenomena.

7. Peter Joseph Wilhelm Debye, 1884—, Dutch-American physicist and chemist; winner of the 1936 Nobel Prize in Chemistry for his work on the structure of molecules; also celebrated for his research on the conductivity of electricity by salt solutions and in the heat capacity of solids.

8. Georgi Dimitrov, 1882–1949, Bulgarian Communist leader; an exile in Berlin in 1933 when arrested and tried by the Nazis for his alleged part in setting the Reichstag on fire (Leipzig Trial, September 21–December 23, 1933). Freed, he went to Moscow, where he served as secretary general of the Communist International from 1934 to the year of its dissolution, 1943. Returning to Bulgaria in 1944 with Soviet troops, he was that country's top Communist leader till his death.

9. Ernst Thaelmann, 1886–1944, German Communist leader; murdered by the Nazis in the Buchenwald concentration camp.

10. Jacques Duclos, 1896—, French Communist leader, for years active in French politics and in the affairs of the Communist International.

II. MISCELLANEOUS ESSAYS
AND SPEECHES

1. *Unity of Science and Technology*

1. The Brown, Boveri and Company plant, founded in 1891 by two young engineers, Charles E. L. Brown, an Englishman, and Walter Boveri, a German, is world-famous as an outstanding maker of turbines, locomotives, and radio transmitters. Brown, Boveri is Switzerland's second largest company (after Nestlé). For an up-to-date account of its success, see *Time* (New York), January 15, 1968, p. 48.
2. Aurel Stodola, 1859–1942, Swiss scientist and engineer of Slovak origin, celebrated for his work on turbines and other machinery.
3. In this article Dr. Kapitsa, in his personal preoccupation with, and ability in, relating science to practical technology, clearly calls for more men on his category to come forth and be given leeway, so that Soviet science and technology could indeed work successfully together. Apparently, in mid-1941, five days before Hitler's attack on the Soviet Union, Soviet science and technology were still not working well together.

2. *The Institute of Problems of Physics*

1. Here is a clear influence of Rutherford upon Kapitsa.
2. See Note 3 to "Introduction. Peter Kapitsa: The Man and His Work."
3. Cryogen is a refrigerant, a substance for obtaining low temperatures.
4. The word "propaganda" used by Dr. Kapitsa in connection with dissemination of scientific knowledge does not generally have in Russian the derogatory connotation it often (almost always!) bears in English and other Western languages.
5. Ernest Werner von Siemens, 1816–92, German inventor and electrical engineer; developer of an electric dynamo and coinventor of an electroplating process; founder and director of Siemens and Halske, the famous electrical apparatus firm. Dr. Kapitsa may have also meant Ernest's brothers, Sir William and Frederick, who, too, were electrical engineers of note.

6. Julius Robert Mayer, 1814–78, German physicist, whose claims to the discovery of conservation of energy are often disputed on the grounds that he was not always adequate or accurate in his reasoning, but whose merit is recognized in the power and insight with which he applied the principle of conservation of energy to numerous physical phenomena.
7. Dmitry K. Chernov, 1839–1921, Russian metallurgist; discoverer of critical temperatures for steel; author of advanced theories on crystallization of steel ingots, heat treatment, cold plastic deformation, and oxidation of metals.
8. Nicholas S. Kurnakov, 1860–1941, Russian chemist; pioneer in physicochemical analysis; researcher in metal alloys, viscosity of binary systems, and thermal analysis; inventor of a self-recording pyrometer; contributor to the refining and production of platinum, aluminum, and magnesium.
9. Nicholas Ye. Zhukovsky, 1847–1921, Russian aeronautical engineer, called by Lenin "the father of Russian aviation"; researcher and contributor in calculations of planes' lifting capacity, wing contours, propellers, hydrodynamics, hydraulics, and aerodynamics.
10. Sergei A. Chaplygin, 1869–1942, Russian physicist, mathematician, and mechanical engineer; a close collaborator with Zhukovsky; contributor to the development of high-speed aviation; researcher in hydromechanics, especially the motion of solids in fluid.
11. Alexander P. Borodin, 1883–87, composer and chemist; author of the opera *Prince Igor* as well as some forty studies on various subjects in chemistry.
12. See Note 4 to "Introduction. Peter Kapitsa: The Man and His Work."

3. Problems of Organizing Scientific Work

No notes of explanation or comment are deemed necessary on this paper.

4. Dimensions of Scientific Work and the Role of the Scientist-Organizer

1. See Note 8 to "The First Two and a Half Years with Rutherford —Young Kapitsa Writes to His Mother."

2. John Desmond Bernal, 1901—, British physicist; specialist on crystallography and biochemistry; left-wing in politics; winner of the 1953 Lenin Peace Prize.

5. *Theory, Experiment, Practice*

1. The importance of this address-essay is analyzed by the editor in his Introduction to this book.
2. The Russian words *moral'*, *moral'nyi*, and *moral'no* pertain to both "morals" and "morale." When Kapitsa speaks of "moral incentives" or "moral conditions" he means that such positive, favorable conditions or circumstances be created for a person's life and work that the person would, as a result, feel a spiritual or emotional satisfaction with his existence and activities— would feel happy not only with his salary, house, and other bodily comforts, but also with the self-esteem and the communal recognition his performance will bring him.
3. The Russian word is *mekhanitsizm* to denote "mechanism" as a doctrine which, according to Webster, "holds natural processes to be mechanically determined and capable of complete explanation by the laws of physics and chemistry."

6. *Effectiveness of Scientific Activity*

1. Here the words "moral influence" mean again the kind of spiritual or emotional satisfaction for Soviet scientists indicated in Note 2 to "Theory, Experiment, Practice."

7. *Mastery of Achievements of Science and Technology*

1. Sir James Dewar, 1842–1923, British (Scottish) chemist and physicist; inventor of vacuum flasks, after which the common thermos bottle is modeled.

Notes

III. TWO INTERVIEWS

1. *Man in the World of Data*

1. Prof. Lev D. Landau, 1908–68, famous Russian physicist, winner of 1962 Nobel Prize, was gravely injured in an automobile accident in January 1962. He was in a deep coma for seven weeks, and on the brink of death for months, but eventually recovered, thanks to the prodigious efforts of some of the world's best neurosurgeons and other medical experts summoned to Moscow from France, Canada, and other countries. (See reference to Landau's imprisonment by Stalin's secret police in the 1930s and his release thanks to Kapitsa's intercession in this book's "Introduction. Peter Kapitsa: The Man and His Work." Also see Landau's biography by Albert Parry in George W. Simmonds, ed., *op. cit.*, pp. 242–248.)
2. Vladimir V. Stasov, 1824–1906, celebrated Russian art and music critic, archeologist, and art historian and librarian, radical in his views, but not a Marxist.
3. See Note 6 on the address on Lomonosov.
4. A large soccer stadium in Moscow.
5. The interviewer used the English word "hobby" in its Russian transliteration "khobby."
6. Sergei T. Aksakov, 1791–1859, Russian writer recently rediscovered by some Soviet intellectuals. He was famous for his calm and realistic depicition of his era's landlords and particularly for the mastery of his descriptions of the Russian landscape.
7. Kapitsa uses this word in its German original.
8. Professor Andrei N. Kolmogorov, 1903–, prominent Soviet mathematician.
9. See Note 3.
10. Regionally and nationally arranged contests for secondary-school Soviet pupils in mathematics and other exact sciences to find gifted candidates for special colleges and universities and thus for lifetime careers in science.
11. Special days for visits and guided tours arranged at some Soviet colleges for likely applicants while they are in the last year of their secondary schools.
12. Italics in this paragraph are in the original of the interview,

apparently to reflect Dr. Kapitsa's own emphasis of the words "ability," "method," and "base."

13. This is a reference to the obligation to do physical labor for at least two years decreed by Nikita Khrushchev in 1958–59 for high school graduates before they could enter college. Soviet scientists and other intellectuals protested this move as a harmful interruption in young people's schooling, and numerous exemptions for gifted youths were won. Since Khrushchev's downfall in October 1964, the two-year requirement of physical labor for high school graduates has been even more widely ignored and officially relaxed almost to a point of abandonment.

14. On the Soviet Russian use of the word "propaganda" see Note 4 to "The Institute of Problems of Physics."

2. *An Invitation to Argument*

1. Dr. Kapitsa, of course, meant 1934, not 1935. He was detained in the Soviet Union on Stalin's orders in the fall of 1934.

2. Karl P. Bryullov, 1799–1852, Russian painter, remembered for the stilted heaviness of his style.

Index

Index

Index

Index

Index

Index

Index

Index